Mrs. E.

Mother Truth's Melodies

Mrs. E. P. Miller

Mother Truth's Melodies

1st Edition | ISBN: 978-3-75241-370-0

Place of Publication: Frankfurt am Main, Germany

Year of Publication: 2020

Outlook Verlag GmbH, Germany.

Reproduction of the original.

MOTHER TRUTH'S MELODIES.

COMMON SENSE FOR CHILDREN.

A KINDERGARTEN,

BY

MRS. E. P. MILLER,

INTRODUCTION.

Since little ones are *geese* no more,
  But *knowing* have become,
It ill beseems that "Mother Goose"
  Should dwell in every home.
So "Mother Truth" in "Melodies"
  For Babes, here lifts her voice,
Assured that parents, children, all,
  Will welcome and rejoice.

{7}

NOTE.

Let no one suppose that the Author of these "Melodies" considers them poetry. They are simply rhymes, the jingle of which may be music in the children's ears, and the illustrations a delight to eager eyes. The Truths presented, even if not fully understood at first, will leave their impress, and in so far as they fill the little minds, will keep out falsehood and false ideas.

The putting of facts in such form as to attract the attention of the little ones, and be readily fixed in their memory, was first suggested to the writer of these rhymes by a valued friend, the well known philanthropist, MRS. ELIZABETH THOMPSON, and her interest in the "Melodies" is such that she has generously assisted in procuring illustrations for the same.

Thus "Mother Truth's Melodies" are introduced with the hope that this effort to entertain children with rhyming reason will meet with the approval of every lover of the young, and of Truth.

{8}

Poetry is the language of the imagination, while "facts are stubborn things," and, in the mass, refuse utterly to be poetized. Yet, even facts may be presented pleasingly and melodiously, and in such way that they will be easily impressed upon the minds of children. This the author of "Mother Truth's Melodies" sought to do, when the little book was first given to the public.

Now, however, in the revising and enlarging of the book, she has given wider play to the imagination, has enlarged the range of subjects, has embodied lessons for children of older growth, and feels that altogether, it will meet more fully the demands which its already large sales warrant her in believing to exist.

She can ask no more favorable reception than was first met; but, hoping for a continuance of the same, she trusts that as it becomes more widely distributed, its truths and teachings will be impressed upon household after household, till throughout the land, the little ones, and larger, too, shall be influenced thereby.

MRS. E. P. M.

{9}

MOTHER TRUTH'S MELODIES.

WHY FLY AWAY, MOTHER GOOSE?

"MOTHER GOOSE, Mother Goose,
 Why fly away?"
"Because Mother Truth is
 A-coming to-day.
She'll tell you funny things,
 But they'll be true;
She'll bring you pictures
 So charming and new;
  She'll sing you Melodies, helping to show
  How, to true women and men, you may grow."

{14}

TOSS THE BABY.

Toss the baby high in air;
Catch him though, with special care
Lest his little back be strained,
Lest his little joints be sprained,
Lest his bones be bent or broken;

Lest through life he bear some token
Of a careless toss or fall,
That for sympathy shall call,
And that must forever be
Painful to our memory.

PAT-A-CAKE, PAT-A-CAKE.

Pat-a-cake, pat-a-cake,
  Mamma's boy,
Laughing and crowing,
  And jumping with joy;
Roll it, and pick it and mark it with B,
  And toss in the oven for Baby and me.

Pat-a-cake, pat-a-cake,
  Papa's girl,
Springing in baby-glee,
  Shaking her curl;
Roll it and pick it and mark it with G,
  And toss in the oven for Girly and me.

HEY, MY KITTEN, MY KITTEN.

Hey, my kitten, my kitten,
  Hey, my kitten, my deary;
If Mamma should feed him too often,
  He never could be so cheery.
  Here we go up, up, up.
And here we go down, down, down-y.
If we never feed baby too much,
  He never will give us a frown-y.

  Hey, my kitten, my kitten,
  Hey, my kitten, my deary;
We'll put him to bed with the birdies,
  And that will make him so cheery!
  Here we go up, up, up,
And here we go down, down, down-y;
If we give him nothing but smiles,
  He will give us never a frown-y.

WINKUM, WINKUM.

Winkum, winkum, shut your eye,
Sweet, my baby, lullaby;
For the dew is falling soft,
Lights are flickering up aloft,
And the head-light's peeping over
Yonder hill-top capped with clover;
Chickens long have gone to rest,
Birds lie snug within their nest,
And my birdie soon will be
Sleeping with the chick-a-dee,
For with only half a try,
Winkum, winkum, shuts her eye.

BABY'S BELL.

Jingle! jingle! baby's bell;
What a tale its tongue might tell.
Could it speak it sure would say,
"When the baby's tired with play,
And is getting cross, don't try
To jingle bells, but hush-a-bye;
All so still, now crooning low,
Lull-a-bye, bye-o, bye-o,—

Quiet down his quaking nerves,
Soothe him as his state deserves;—
Passing hand from head to feet,
Sl-o-w-l-y, softly, loving, sweet,
As to smooth the feathers down,
Rumpled, from your birdling's crown;—   {19}   See, he sleeps,
and in his dream
Yours may hand of angel seem,
Raveling out the tangled ills,
Knitting up with restful thrills."

WILLY-NILLY.

Willy-Nilly, birdy sings,
  For he's running over
With the music that he flings
  To his sweet bird-lover;—
Willy-nilly, baby laughs,
 Gay and glad and gleeful;
Brimming over high with health,
  She is always playful.

{20}

BABY'S RECORD.

New-born baby, soft and pink,
Of the two worlds on the brink.

One month old,—eat and sleep;
Precious little human heap.

Two months old,—tear and smile;
Fists in mouth and eyes the while.

Three months old,—"goo-a-goo,"
Windows wide where soul looks through.

Four months old,—finds his toes,
Tries to fix them on his nose.   {21}
Five months old,—first wee pearl;
All the household in a whirl.

Six months old,—sits alone;
Wishes swaddling clothes were gone.

Seven months old,—creep and crawl,
Wonder-eyed, a charm to all.

Eight months old,—confiscate
Pussy's tail and papa's pate.

Nine months old,—roguish eyes
Deepening daily; wilful, wise.

Ten months old,—witching ways
Wind us in; the baby pays!

Eleven months old,—finger-tip
Guides the elfin on his trip.

Year old,—lots of mischief done;
Walking, talking, just for fun.

{22}

SLEEP, LITTLE SWEETEY.

Sleep now, my sweetey,
Dear one, and pretty!
Weary with playing,
Weary with straying,
Stop little thinkers,
Shut little winkers;
Sleep, little sweetey,
Precious and pretty.

Sleep now, my sweetey,
Dear One, and pretty!
Stop little thinkers,
Shut little winkers,
Angels a-watching
Sleep-doors unlatching;
Slip in, my sweetey,
Precious and pretty!

Sleeping, my sweetey,
Dear one, and pretty!
Stopped, little thinkers,
Shut, little winkers,
Angels a-watching,
Sleep-doors are latching;
Slipped in, my sweetey,
Precious and pretty!

{23}

NEVER TELL A FIB.

If mamma says she'll punish,
   She must do it, or she tells
A fib, as Sister Annie
   Told "a story" 'bout the bells;
And if mamma tells a fib,
   Then surely children will,
And what a fearful thing,
   Our home with fibs to fill!

{24}

HUMPTY—DUMPTY.

Humpty-Dumpty, hip-o'-to-hop,
Baby is crying, why doesn't he stop?
What does he cry for? his clothing is tight;

No wonder such things make baby a fright.

   Humpty-dumpty, hip-o'-to-hop,
Baby was crying, but now he will stop;
What did he cry for? his clothing was wet;
No wonder such things should make babies fret.

   Humpty-dumpty, hip-o'-to-hop,
Baby is crying, oh, when will he stop?
What does he cry for? his feet are a-cold;
No wonder such things should make baby scold.   {25}
   Humpty-dumpty, hip-o'-to-hop,
Baby is crying, but soon he will stop;
What does he cry for? he had too much food;
No baby in this way can ever be good.

   Humpty-dumpty, hip-o'-to-hop,
Baby is laughing and scarcely will stop;
What does he laugh for? Oh, when he feels well,
He always is happy,—'tis thus we can tell.

{26}

HUSH-A-BYE.

Hush-a-bye, baby,
  On Grandmother's lap;
Hush-a-bye, baby,

And take a nice nap;
Hush-a-bye, baby,
  What is it you say?
Your "teeth are a-coming,"
You're "ten months to-day;"
Well, babies must cry,
And Grandmothers must try
To comfort and hush them, but never forget
  The little gums ache,
  And little nerves quake,
Till little lips quiver, and babies must fret.

Hush-a-bye, baby,
  We'll cool his hot gums,
Hush-a-bye, baby,
  With tiny ice-crumbs;
Hush-a-bye, baby,
  We'll rub hard and long
With icy-cold finger,—
  See him list to my song! {27}
Ah, babies are sweet
If their wants we but meet,
So why should we blame them when fretful and cross?
  Let us find what is wrong,
  And remove it ere long,
And we'll see that time thus spent is never a loss.

Hush-a-bye, baby,
  What more can we do
Hush-a-bye, baby,
  That will comfort you?
Hush-a-bye, baby,
  We'll lay you down flat,
On your stomach, dear baby,
  On Grandmother's lap. {28}
  Nor trot you a mite,
  No matter how slight,
But, sure that your clothing is all dry and neat,
  We'll loosen each band,
  And with soft and warm hand,

Gently rub you all over from head to your feet.

Hush-a-bye, baby,
  We will not forget,
Hush-a-bye, baby,
  That hands may be wet,
Hush-a-bye, baby,
  And soothe you sometimes,
When dry hands won't do it,
  Hush, list to my rhymes! {29}
  And now we'll not nurse
  Till the nursing's a curse;
Nor dose you, nor drug you, nor feed with sweet-meats,
  Nor to soothe, will we try,
  With old "Dame Winslow" by,
For our hopes for the babies, she ever defeats.

Hush-a-bye, baby,
  We'll quiet his nerves,
Hush-a-bye, baby,
  The truth it deserves—
Hush-a-bye, baby—
  Even here to be known :
We will *quiet his nerves*   By *just calming our own!* And our
baby will feel
  The sweet hush o'er him steal,
That brings with it soothing and comfort and rest;
And to slumber so soft,
His spirit we'll waft,
And then lay him away in his own baby nest.

{30}

DON'T MAKE ME LAUGH.

Dear Mamma, I've been laughing
    For Uncle Ben and Pa,
And then for sister Lizzie
    I talked "ar-g o-o" and "gar;"
And then a "little story"
    For Dick and Cousin Jane,—
And now you, Mamma, want me
    To laugh and talk again.

I'd like to do it,
    Mamma, but if I even try,
I am so weary with it,
    I'm sure I'd only cry!
Don't let them try, dear Mamma,
    to make me laugh and crow,
I'll do it when I'm able,
    for babies always do.

{31}

BYE-BABY-BUNTING.

BYE-BABY-BUNTING,
The Indians live by hunting,
And bring home many a beaver-skin
To wrap the little pappoose in.
And mother-squaw the baby'll tie
Fast on a board, and swinging high,
Will hang it up among the trees
To rock-a-bye with every breeze;
But our dear baby, snug and warm,
Shall rock-a-bye on mother's arm.

{32}

TO BED WITH THE CHICKENS.

Oh, put me in my bed, Mamma,
  When chickens go to rest,
For I'm your little chick-a-dee,
  So put me in my nest.

Yes, when the birds forget to sing,
  And lambs forget to play,
You'll put your birdy in his nest,
  Your lamb you'll fold away.

{33}

DIVE ME SUDAR.

Papa, when you dive me tandy,
  Dive me only white,—
'Tause there's poison in the tolored,
  Which my health will blight;
But you better dive me sudar,
  Let the tandy be,—
'Tause I shall not want so much,
  And that is best for me.

{34}

'TAUSE I'M TROSS

Mamma, 'tause I'm tross don't whip me;
  I tan't help it, not a bit!
'Tis the tandy hurts my stomat,
  And that mates me whine and fret.
Sometimes, too, I'm whipped for trossness

When the trossness tomes from meat; {35} Thint how
tiders drowl and drumble,
    And then dive me food to eat
  That will mate me well and happy,—
    Wheat and oat-meal, rice and truit,
  These will mate me dood and gentle,
    'Stead of mating me a brute.

{36}

THE NEW BOOK.

COCK-A-DOODLE-DOO,
A picture-book for you,—
Keep it nice, and in a trice
Sing Cock-a-doodle-doo.

{37}

WHISKUM, WHISKUM.

Whiskum, whiskum, over the house,
Scud the cloudlets, still as a mouse;
Whiskum, whiskum, by-and-by
They'll pour rain-drops from the sky.

THE JACK-HORSE.

We will ride our Jack-horse
All the meadows across;
  Oh no, do not whip him,
  But feed him, my dear!
A handful of grass
In his mouth as we pass,
  Will make him trot gaily,
  And give us good cheer!

{39}

HI-DIDDLE-DIDDLE.

HI-DIDDLE-DIDDLE
Mother duck's in the middle,
Her baby-ducks swimming around;
  With bills like a ladle,
  And feet like a paddle,
No danger that they will be drowned

{40}

THE RAIN.

Come, rain, come,
  That the water may run,
That the meadow grass may grow;
  That the fruit and grain
  O'er hill and plain,
May greet us as we go.

Come, rain, come,
  That the water may run,
That the mill may make our meal;—
  'Twill grind our wheat,
  And corn so sweet,
When it turns the old mill-wheel.

{41}

FEED THE BIRDIES.

Feed the birdies, darling,
  When the snow is here,
When there are no berries
  On the bushes, dear;—
Scatter food out for them,
  And they'll quickly come,
Hopping, singing, chirping
  "Thank you for the crumb."

{42}

ROCK-A-BYE.

Rock-a-bye, baby,
  Our darling is ill,
Rock-a-bye, baby,
  We'll soon have him well;—
Rock-a-bye, baby,
  Don't tremble with fear,
For that tends to make
  His slight illness severe.

Rock-a-bye, baby,

Our darling is ill.
Rock-a-bye, baby,
  We'll soon have him well;—
Rock-a-bye, baby.
  Don't coax him to nurse,
For urging to eat
  Only makes matters worse.   {43}
Rock-a-bye, baby,
  Our darling is ill,
Rock-a-bye, baby,
  We'll soon have him well;—
Rock-a-bye, baby,
  No company 'round,
Not even the dear ones,
  To make a loud sound.

Rock-a-bye, baby,
  Our darling is ill,
Rock-a-bye, baby,
  We'll soon have him well;—
Rock-a-bye, baby,
 Don't rattle the papers
Nor whisper around,
  Little nerves cut such capers.   {44}
Rock-a-bye, baby,
  Our darling is ill,
Rock-a-bye, baby
  We'll soon have him well;—
Rock-a-bye, baby,
  Whatever is wrong,
Attend to his bowels,
  Neglected too long,

Rock-a-bye, baby,
  Our darling is ill,
Rock-a-bye, baby,
  We'll soon have him well;—
Rock-a-bye, baby,
  If he is too hot,
Undress him and bathe him;
  But, ah! he is not.

Rock-a-bye, baby,
  Our darling is ill,
Rock-a-bye, baby,
  We'll soon have him well;—
Rock-a-bye, baby,
  There is cough with unrest,
So we'll wring out hot flannels,
  And cover his chest, {45}
Rock-a-bye, baby,
  Our darling is ill;
Rock-a-bye, baby,
  We'll soon have him well;—
Rock-a-bye, baby,
  He's perspiring, to pour!
We will keep up this treatment
  A full hour more.

Rock-a-bye, baby,
  Our darling is ill,
Rock-a-bye, baby,
  We'll soon have him well;—
Rock-a-bye, baby,
  Now dry him off neat,
And wrap him up warm,
  And to-morrow, repeat. {46}
Rock-a-bye, baby,
  Our darling is ill,
Rock-a-bye, baby,
  We'll soon have him well;—
Rock-a-bye, baby,
  'Tis not in his chest?
Then place the hot flannels
  Where he feels the unrest.

Rock-a-bye, baby,
  Our darling is ill,
Rock-a-bye, baby,
  We'll soon have him well;—
Rock-a-bye, baby,
  He is moaning with pain,
And rolling his head,
  And we pet him in vain.

Rock-a-bye, baby,
  Our darling is ill;
Rock-a-bye, baby,
  We'll soon have him well;—
Rock-a-bye, baby,
  We will wring out from ice,
Linen cloths for his head,
  All so cooling and nice.   {47}
Rock-a-bye, baby,
  Our darling is ill;
Rock-a-bye, baby,
  We'll soon have him well;
Rock-a-bye, baby,
  If cold don't relieve,
Use hot and then cold,
  And then hot, you perceive.

Rock-a-bye, baby,
  Our darling is ill;
Rock-a-bye, baby,
  We'll soon have him well;—
Rock-a-bye, baby,
  We'll see that his feet
Are kept warm all the time,
  And his clothes dry and neat.   {48}
Rock-a-bye, baby,
  Our darling was ill
Rock-a-bye, baby,
  But now he is well;
Rock-a-bye, baby,
  No drugs, not a dose!
Yet he's over it finely,
  Just hear how he crows

{49}

THE SNOWBALL.

Have ever you seen how a wee bit of snow,
To a big bouncing ball, just by rolling, will grow?
'Tis thus our wee sins, children, let to roll on,
Will grow big, bigger, biggest, till Satan has won.

{50}

LITTLE BO-PEEP.

Co' Nan, co' Nan, says little Bo-peep,
Co' Nan, co' Nan, up come the sheep;
They jump the ditch and scale the wall,
Where one sheep goes, they follow, all.

Co' dea', co' dea', says little Bo-peep,
Co' dea', co' dea', I'll shear my sheep;
Their wool so fine will make my coat,
My blankets and my hose to boot.

{51}

THE TEA-PARTY.

Ah! little ones, I'm sure there's not
A drop of tea in your weeny pot.
For water bright and milk so pure,
Alone will bring you health, be sure;
And health is beauty, health is cheer,
Health is happiness so dear.

{52}

TELL IT AGAIN, MOTHER.

"Tell it again, Mother,
  Tell it again,"—
No matter what story she told
  We children, would cry,
  In the days gone by.
Before our years were old.

"Tell it again, Mother,
  Tell it again,"—
No matter how weary and worn.
  For we children knew naught
  Of the care we brought,
Before our sense was born. {53}
  "Tell it again, Mother,
  Tell it again,"—
And she, patient, and kind, and wise,
  The tale would repeat,
  Or the song so sweet,
And 'twas ever a glad surprise.

"Tell it again, Mother,
  Tell it again,"—
Ah! you children, when children no more,
  Will go back to the days
  Of sweet babyhood lays,
And Mother's sage sayings con o'er.

{54}

LITTLE JACK HORNER.

```
LITTLE JACK HORNER
   Sat in the corner,
Eating a morsel of nice brown bread;
   "Have some pie, or some cake?"
   "Nay, not I," with a shake
And a toss of his wise little head.
   "For this bread will make bone,
   And white teeth like a stone,
That will neither grow soft nor decay;
   But rich cake and rich pie
   Sure will break, bye and bye,
My good health, and that never will pay."
```

{55}

LITTLE BOY BLUE.

```
"Little Boy Blue, may I go with you now?"
"Yes, down to the pasture to drive up the cow."

"Little boy blue, what then may I have?"
A nice cup of milk as ever cow gave.

"Little boy blue, the milk must be set;"
"Yes, for 'tis thus the nice cream we shall get."

"Little boy blue, what will we do then?"
"We'll skim it and dash it, with 'churn, butter, churn.'"

"Little boy blue, what else can we make?"
"O, cheese, tempting cheese, and the dainty cheese cake."

"Little boy blue, is there anything more?"
"O, yes, puddings, custards and dainties, a store."

"Little boy blue, shall we eat of all these?"
"Simple food is far better for us, if you please."
```

{56}

MISS VELVET-PAWS.

Little Miss Velvet-paws,
Raveling out her yarn,
Catches mice, in a trice,
In everybody's barn.

Look out for velvet paws,
Do not trust them far,
For velvet paws cover claws
That will leave a scar.

{57}

POLLY HOPKINS.

Now little Polly Hopkins
Must surely know great A,
And B, and C, and D, and E,
   F, G, H, I, J, K;
And L, and M, and N, and O,
And P, and Q, R, S,
And T, U, V, and W, X,
   And Y, & Z, I guess.

{58}

A, B, C.

A Stands for Alligator,

B Stands for Ball,

C Stands for Cat in a cream-pot,

D Stands for Doll.

{59}

E Stands for East, or Ellen.

F Stands for Fay,

G Stands for Goat, a
Pen in,

H Stands for Hay,

I Stands for Indigestion,

{60}

J Stands for Jar,

K Stands for King, or Keepsake,

L Stands for La,

M Stands for Man, or Thousand,

N Stands for Nail,

{61}

O Stands for Oaken bucket,

P Stands for Pail,

Q Stands for Queen, or Question.

R Stands for Rose,

S Stands for Christmas Stocking,

{62}

T Stands for Toes,

U Stands for Urn, or Ulster,

V Stands for Vane,

W Stands for West, or Winter.

{63}

X Stands for Ten.

Y Stands for Yoke,
(with Oxen).

Z Stands for Zero.

& when you've learned your LETTERS,
You'll be a Hero.

{64}

C-A-T spells CAT,
  That brought the kittens here;

D-O-G spells DOG,
  That does, the puppies, rear.

C-O-W, Cow,
  The mother of the calf;

O-X spells the Ox,
  That's bigger, yes, by half.

{65}

B-O-Y spells BOY,
  That's little brother Lou;

G-I-R-L, GIRL,
  And that is sister Sue.

B-I-R-D, BIRD,
  Just hear canary sing;

G-O-L-D, GOLD,
  That makes a handsome ring

B-O-O-K, BOOK,
  In which we learn to read;

C-O-O-K, COOK,
  Supplies the food we need.

{66}

S-E-E-D, SEED,
  From which we raise the plant;

S-I-N-G, SING,
  Just hear the children chant.

B-A, BA, B-Y, BY,
  And that spells BABY, love;

L-A, LA, D-Y, DY,
  And that spells LADY, dove.

M-A, MA, R-Y, RY,
  And that spells MARY, child,

E-D, ED, D-Y, DY,
  That's EDDY, sweet and mild.

{67}

THE KITTEN.

ONE, two, (1, 2,)
  Here's a kitten for you;

THREE, four, (3, 4,)
  She will open the door,

FIVE, six, (5, 6,)
  And your cream she will mix,—

{68}

```
SEVEN, eight, (7, 8,)
  If you are too late,

NINE, ten, (9, 10,)
  To cover the pan;

ELEVEN, twelve, (11, 12,)
  And then you must delve,—

THIRTEEN, fourteen, (13, 14,)
  To cover her sporting;

FIFTEEN, Sixteen, (15, 16,)
  But while you are fixing,-  {69}
SEVENTEEN, eighteen, (17, 18,)
  Remember I'm waiting,

NINETEEN, twenty, (19, 20,)
  For butter a plenty.
```

* * * * *

To those who serve you, children, all,
  Be gentle and polite,—
For thus are gentle-women known,
  Or gentle-men, at sight.

{70}

DOLLY DIMPLE.

DOLLY DIMPLE, just for fun,
Stands to show us she is ONE.

Dolly and her sister Sue
Show that ONE and ONE make Two.

{71}

Dolly, Sue, and Nanny Lee,
Show that ONE with TWO make THREE.

Doll, Sue, Nan, and little Noah,
Show that ONE with THREE make FOUR.

{72}

Doll, Sue, Nan, Noah, and Ben Brive
Show that ONE with FOUR make FIVE.

Now all these with Jenny Hicks
Show that ONE with FIVE make SIX.

{73}

One more, Ned, a baby, even,
Shows that ONE with SIX make SEVEN.

With these girls and boys, put Kate,
And the ONE with SEVEN make EIGHT.

{74}

All these eight, with Adaline
Show that ONE with EIGHT make NINE.

Now with these put Dick, and then
You'll see that ONE with NINE make TEN.

{75}

IF YOU PLEASE.

I hope my children never will
    Say, "Give me" this or that,—
But, "If you please," I'd like a bun,
    Or, "Thank you" for a pat.

{76}

THE POOR LITTLE CHICK-A-DEES.

TEN little chick-a-dees clinging to a vine,—
A speckled snake charmed *one*, then there were but NINE.

NINE little chick-a-dees,—one without a mate,—
A Sparrow-hawk caught *one*,then there were but EIGHT.

{77}

EIGHT little chick-a dees, by a 'possum driven,—
He caught *one* and slaughtered it, then there were but SEVEN.

SEVEN little chick-a-dees hopping round the ricks,—
A Weasel came and captured *one*, then there were but six.

SIX little chick-a-dees watching Rover dive,—
He sprang ashore and seized *one*, then there were but FIVE.

{78}

FIVE little chick-a-dees pecking at the door,
Kitty-cat caught *one*, then there were but FOUR.

FOUR little chick-a-dees full of birdy glee,
One was tangled in a net, then there were but THREE.

THREE little chick-a-dees dabbling in the dew,
A stone fell and crushed *one*, then there were but TWO.

{79}

TWO little chick-a-dees peeping just for fun,
A hungry Kite caught *one*, then there was but ONE.

ONE little chick-a-dee, mourning all alone,
Flew away to find a mate, and then there was NONE,

{80}

HEIGH-HO, DAISIES AND BUTTER-CUPS.

HEIGH-HO, daisies and butter-cups
Grow in the meadows for children to gather;
But cattle will shun them,
And farmers will burn them,
Because in their fields they are only a bother.

Heigh-ho, red-top and clover-bloom,
Filling the air with their sweetness and beauty,
Will yield without measure,

Their wealth of rich treasure,
Rewarding the farmer for doing his duty.

{81}

THE PONY.

Once 2 is 2,
  Here's a pony for you;

Two 2s are 4,
  But be careful the more,—

THREE 2s are 6,
  For perhaps pony kicks;
FOUR 2s are 8,
  And if so we must wait,

{82}

FIVE 2s are 10,
  Till he's trained by the men;—

Six 2s are 12,
  Before trusting ourselves,

{83}

SEVEN 2s are 14,
  To ride him out sporting;

EIGHT 2s are 16,

But we can be fixing

NINE 2s are 18,
  His food while we're waiting;

TEN 2s are 20,
  Oh, yes, give him plenty,—

ELEVEN 2s are 22,
  For then he will be gentle to—   {84}
TWELVE 2s are 24,
  Us who feed and pet him more.

{85}

{86}

BABY'S RECKONING.

One little head, Ah! but what does it hold?
No matter,—it's worth its whole weight in pure gold.

Two big brown eyes, soft with Heaven's own dew;
No diamonds so precious, so sparkling, so true.   {87}
Three cunning dimples, one deep in her chin,
And one in each cheek—Ah! they're just twin and twin.

Four little fingers to clutch mamma's hair,
But sweeter than honeycomb, even when there.

Five, we may call it, with little Tom Thumb,
And that fist in her mouth is as sweet as a plum.

Six wonderful pearls her bright coral lips hide,
And the Kohinoor's nothing these pure pearls beside.

Seven brown wavelets are ever in motion,
And silken floss to them is naught, to our notion.

Eight little giggles run over with glee—
And more if you call them, so merry is she.

Nine songs, (they're Greek tho' to all but mamma),
Make us think she is destined, an Opera Star.

Ten toddling steps, but to us full of grace,
For our babe in our hearts ever holds the first place.

TWO LITTLE PINK SHOES.

Two little pink shoes standing by the head
Of our Nanny sleeping in the trundle-bed;

On the little table, waiting for the morn,
Two little pink shoes, our Nanny to adorn.   {89}
Two little bright eyes, peeping open wide,
Spied the little table, and the pink shoes spied.

Two little fat hands climbing up to catch;
Two little fat feet following to match.

Two little fat arms hug them to her breast;
Two little fat legs run to show the rest.

Never more a treasure can our Nancy choose,
That will give such pleasure as these two pink shoes.

* * * * *

In your work or your play,
   When you read, talk, or write,
Sit always, my child,
   With your back to the light,

BABY PEARL.

Now listen while I tell you, child,
   That I am quite a grown-up girl,
For I can read, and spell my name,
   While you,—why, you're just Baby Pearl.

I help mamma to "house-keep," too,
   Although she says I make a whirl!
But I can wipe the forks and spoons,
   While you, Ah, you're just Baby Pearl.

And then I dress myself, you see,
   And comb my hair when not in curl,
And I can make my dolly's clothes,
   While you, you're only Baby Pearl.   {91}
Tis true, mamma says I must be
   "A very pattern little girl,"
Just all for you, and I shall try
   Because, because, you're Baby Pearl.

44

* * * * *

MY VALENTINE.

Dearest little lover mine,
  Sweetest, pertest valentine;
"Desht I'm two years old," he says,—
Blessings on his pretty ways,—

"'Tan't I be your valentine?"
Yes forever, lover mine,
Shalt thou be my valentine.

{92}

FEE-FI-FO-FUM.

FEE-FI-FO-FUM,
From the Spruce-tree comes the gum;
From the Pine the turpentine,
  Tar and pitch,
  And timber which
Is very choice and fine.

  Fee-fi-fo-fum,
How from Spruce-tree comes the gum?
Soft enough;—the sticky stuff,
  From seam and cleft,
  Both right and left,
Flows out, and hardens, rough.   {93}
  Fay-fi-fo-fee,
Nut-galls grow on the Oak-tree;
By tiny worms the nut-gall forms,
  Like little ball;
  And from Nut-gall
The Gallic Acid comes.

Fee-fi-fo-fade,
From Nut-galls, too, the Tannin's made;
While Acorns grow in group or row;—
  And Live-oak long,
  Makes ship-knees, strong,
That round the world may go.

{94}

Fee-fi-fo-fap,
We tap the Maples, and the sap
We find as sweet as sugar-beet,
  Then boiling hard,
  Our sure reward,
The maple-sugar treat.

{95}

Fay-fi-fo-fee,
See the graceful White-Birch tree,
With bark so light, so tough and tight
  That Indians wrought
  Canoes we're taught,
And paddled out of sight.

{96}

Fee-fi-fo-fap,
Hark and hear the Hemlock snap;—
Little spine so full of wind,
  Heated, hops,
  And jumping, pops,
And makes the bright eyes shine.

Fee-fi-fo-fur,
See the curious chestnut-burr;
Green and round, then turning brown.
  Frost opens wide
  Each prickly side,
And out the chestnuts bound.

```
Fee-fi-fo-fay,
Now the farmer makes his hay;
Grasses grow, which workmen mow,—
  Toss every-wise,
  Till sunshine dries,
Then into stacks, they stow.
```

```
Fay-fee-fi-fo,
See the farmer wield his hoe,
Lettuce, greens, then corn and beans,
  With pumpkin-vines
  Along the lines,
Where many a weed o'er-leans.
```

{98}

```
Fee-fi-fo-fog,
See the wriggling pollywog,*—
With funny tail; but without fail
  This pollywog
  Will grow a frog,
And lose his wiggle-tail.
```

[Footnote: Pollywog—Common name for poll wig, or tadpole.]

```
Fee-fi-fo-faint,
Colors, seven, the Rainbow paint;
Violet bright is first in sight—
  Then indigo,
  Blue, green, yellow,
Orange and Red,—the seven, WHITE.
```

{99}

```
Fay-fee-fi-fo,
Now you ask, "What makes Rainbow?"
```

It is the sun, my darling one,
  Shines through the rain,
  O'er hill and plain,
But see, the beauty's flown.

  Fay-fi-fo-fear,
Don't you understand it, dear?
Raindrops fall, Sun shines through all,
  Reflects beyond,
  This beauteous wand
Which we the Rainbow call.

{100}

THE OXEN.

The oxen are such clever beasts,
  They'll drag the plough all day;
They're very strong and tug along
  Great loads of wood or hay.

They feed on grass, when green or dry;
  Their flesh is beef, for food;
Their lungs are "lights," their stomach, "tripe,"
  Their skin for leather's good.

Their hair men use in mortar, too,
  Lime, water, sand and hair,
They nicely mix and smoothly fix,
  For plastering, so fair.

{101}

For making soap their bones are used;
  Their horns for combs we group;
Their feet are boiled for "neat's-foot-oil,"
  Their tails for ox-tail soup.

Their heart-case forms a money-bag;
  Their tallow, candles, white;
Their intestine, gold-beater's skin,
  With which gold-leaf we smite.

Thus every part is useful made;
  The same is true of cows,—
Except their ilk gives luscious milk
  Instead of dragging ploughs.

{102}

Oxen and cows are "cattle" called;
  They go in "herds," when wild;
But when they're tame, by other name,—
  A "drove," *en masse*, they're styled.

Their little ones are "calves,"—and cows'
  Rich milk produces cream,
Which butter makes, and nice cheese-cakes,
  With curd, whey, and caseine.

And now 'tis funny, but 'tis true,
  Some children young and mazy,
Have thought their eyes were used some-wise,
  To make the ox-eyed daisy! {103}
This cannot be, yet creatures' bones
  Placed round trees, plants and bowers,
Will serve to feed just what they need,
  To grow fine fruits and flowers.

THE BROKEN PITCHER.

"Sweet, my love, I'm sorry
    That you did not tell,
When you broke the pitcher
    Coming from the well."

"Oh, I thought you'd whip me,
    Just as Betty did;
Then when she would ask me,
    I would tell a fib."

"Sweet, my child, I never
    Punish any one
For an accidental
    Thing that may be done.

"Tell me always, darling,
    Everything you do;
This will help to make you
    Thoughtful, brave and true."

{105}

THE ELEPHANTS.

THE ivory for our combs,
  From elephants' tusks is made;
The handles, too for many a knife,
  And for paper-knives the blade.

The elephant knows a friend,—
  And well remembers, too,
A kindly act, but ne'er forgets
  The teasing of a foe.

{106}

THE WIND.

"What is the wind, Mamma?"
  "Tis air in motion, child;"
"Why can I never see the wind
  That blows so fierce and wild?"

"Because the Gases, dear,
  Of which the air is made,
Are quite transparent, that is, we
  See through, but see no shade."

"And what are Gases, Ma?"
  "Fluids, which, if we squeeze
In space too small, will burst with force;"—
  "And what are *fluids*, please?"

"Fluids are what will flow,
    And gases are so light
That when we give them room enough,
    They rush with eager flight."

{107}

"What gases, dear Mamma,
    Make up the air or wind?"
"'Tis Oxygen and Nitrogen
    That chiefly there we find;
And when the air is full
    Of Oxygen we're gay,
But when there is not quite enough,
    We're dull, or faint away."

THE FOG.

"What is the fog, Mamma?"
    "Sometimes the air is light
And cannot bear up all the mists,
    And then 'tis foggy, quite;

But when air heavier grows,
    The fog is borne above,
And floated off, the cloudy stuff,—
    Just see it, graceful, move."

{108}

THE RAIN.

"What makes the rain, Mamma?"
    "The mists and vapors rise
From land and stream and rolling sea,
    Up toward the distant skies;

And there they form the clouds,
　　Which, when they're watery, dear,
Pour all the water down to earth,
　　And rain afar or near."

THE SNOW.

"What makes the Snow, Mamma?"
　　"When very cold above,
The mists are frozen high in air,
And fall as snow, my love."　{109}
"And Hail?" "Tis formed the same;
　　Cold streams of air have come
And frozen all the water-drops,
　　And thus the hail-stones form.

"Now do not question more,
　　Dear child, but run and play,
I'll tell you of the Water, Fire,
　　And Light, another day."
"Oh yes, and dear Mamma,
　　Of Thunder, Lightning, too,
For I shall want to know it all,
　　So tell me, Mamma, do."

TRUTH.

Do not let "Mother Truth" find a falsehood all over,—
  Amongst all her children, no, never a lie;
Stand for Truth, ye wee babies, for Truth, ye who're older,
  For Truth while you live, and for Truth till you die.

All ye myriads of children this little book talks to,
  Form now in each household a band for the Truth,
Do not let even a "white lie," and still less a "whopper,"
  Find a place in your hearts, nor your heads, nor your mouth.

You know God is Truth;—and as you are His children,
  You want to be like Him as near as you can;
Speak the Truth, live the Truth, be the Truth with Him,
  And Heaven will have come, as Christ taught in his plan.

HI-DIDDLE, HO-DIDDLE.

HI-DIDDLE, HO-DIDDLE,
  Pop-diddle-dee,
This Earth of ours, on which we live,
Is round as it can be.
  Pray, then, what is a
  Mountain, valley, hill?
They are but like little warts,
And pores, on orange-peel.

  Hi-diddle, ho-diddle,
  Pop-diddle-dee,—
Our Earth is swinging in the air,
As you can plainly see;— {113}   Pray, then, what keeps it
  Hanging up in space?
The Sun, my child, attracts the Earth
And holds it in its place.

Hi-diddle, ho-diddle,
  Pop-diddle-dee,

A lovely Moon is shining for
This Earth of ours, you see,—
   Held in its cradle
   Ever since its birth,
Because our globe attracted it,
As the Sun attracts the Earth.

   Hi-diddle, ho-diddle,
   Pop-diddle-dee,
What I mean by globe, child,
You're wondering now, I see.   {114}   A globe or a ball, dear,

Is what is round and true,
And that is why I'm calling it,
This Earth, a globe, to you.

  Hi-diddle, ho-diddle,
  Pop-diddle-dee,
Instead of globe I might have said
A *sphere* for you and me;
  For all the same, in truth,
  Are sphere and globe and ball,
And *hemi*'s half so half this Earth,
A *hemisphere*, we call.

  Hi-diddle, ho-diddle,
  Pop-diddle-dee,
'T was once supposed the Earth stood still,
While Sun went round it, free;—
  But now we've learned it well,
  That 't is the Earth doth turn
Upon its Axis, as it's called;
And also round the Sun.

{115}

  Hi-diddle, ho-diddle,
  Pop-diddle-dee,
Our Earth in turning round,
How long may she be?
  She turns on her axis
  In a day, and a night,
But to go around the Sun
Takes a year for the flight.

{116}

WHAT IS THE AXIS?

  Now you ask, "What is the Axis?"
  With an apple I will show;
Place your thumb upon the stem-place,
  And your finger at the blow;—
Now we'll just suppose the apple
  Has a stem that passes through,
And this stem would be the Axis;
  Now we'll whirl the apple, true,

  Holding fast 'twixt thumb and finger,—
  That's the way the Earth goes round
On its Axis, as we call it,
  Though no real stem is found.   {117} And the two ends of
the Axis

58

Have been called the Poles, my dear;
Yes, the North Pole and the South Pole,
   Where 'tis very cold and drear.

Now we'll hold a bigger apple
   At a distance, for the Sun;
Tip the smaller one a little,
   And then slowly wheel it round
All around the larger apple,
   And it represents the Earth
Circling round the Sun that holds it,
   Ceaseless, in its yearly path.

Wondrous is the strong attraction
   Of the Sun which holds in place
All the Planets in their turnings,
   All the Stars that see his face;
But more wondrous far the power
   That created Sun and us,
And that gave a form and being,
   To this mighty Universe.

"The Universe!" now you exclaim:
   "By the Universe, what do you mean?"   {118}   'Tis
the Sun and the Planets, and every thing known,
   That we call by this Universe name.

Now the "Planets," you ask,
   "What are Planets?" They're globes,
Some larger, some smaller than Earth,—
   Which are swinging in space,
   And are all held in place,
By the God-power that first gave them birth.

{119}

HEAT AND COLD.

Our earth has a *North Pole*,
   Where 'tis very cold;
It also has a *South Pole*,
   That's just the same, we're told.
But half-way between,
   And all the way around,
We call it the *Equator*,
   And heat doth there abound.
For there the sun shines always,
   Though it goes north or south

Some twenty-three degrees or more,
  And sometimes causes drouth.
The sun goes north, we call it.
  But 'tis the earth instead,
That tips, and makes it seem the sun
  Comes higher overhead.
And when the sun is northward
  'Tis summer here, you see;
And when it's to the southward
  'Tis there in same degree.

{120}

HARLEY'S DREAM.

I know a little brown-eyed boy,
  His name is Harley Hart;
And with a naughty boy or girl,
  Our Harley has no part.

He cons his lessons o'er and o'er,
  And once he fell asleep,
With finger marking A, B, C,
  As 'twere the place to keep.

And then he dreamed a funny dream—
  The page jumps up to dance,
The letters laugh, and by and by,
  Like imps they leap and prance.   {121}
Now Harley oft had wondered whence
  The letters first had come;
And I'm afraid he sometimes wished
  They all had staid at home,

Instead of teasing him with quirks,
  And bothering him with names
That seemed to help him hardly more
  In learning words than games.

One little imp squeaked: "I am *A;*   You could not be a man
Without me." Then another cried:
  "I am E" and quickly ran,

Exclaiming: "And without us both
  You could not have a head."
Another says: "You'd have no limbs
  If *I* were lost or dead."

Then *O*, "You'd have no nose nor toes,
  If it were not for me;"
"And what is more, were I not here,"
  Says *U*, "you could not be."   {122}
And thus they each and all lay claim
  To parcel and to part
Of what he was, or what should do
  With hand, or head, or heart.

They hung a ladder 'gainst the tree,
  And clambered up and down;
They played a thousand pranks as wild
  As any gipsey clown.

They whispered that they came from Rome,
  And that, if rightly placed,
They'd serve our Harley with a feast
  A king would joy to taste.

So when he woke and knew they were
  The little mystic keys
That open Learning's gates so wide,
  He loved his A, B, C's.

]

{123}
OUR LANGUAGE KEY.

A E I O U Y

We are small, and we are few,
But we're wondrous mighty, too,—
For no word can language wear,
Save in it we hold a share.
One of us in May is met,—
One is caught in every net;
One is in the clambering vine,
One, in Moon, must ever shine;
One's in you,—and all so shy,
The last is hiding in your eye.

{124}

THE SPEECH FAMILY.

The name of everything we know,
as *slate*, or *book*, or *toy*,
Is called a *Noun*.
All names are nouns; remember this, my boy.

A word that means to be,
to act, or to be acted on,
Is called a *Verb*; as *is*,
or *eat*, or *sing*; or he *is gone*.   {125}
A word that tells the color, form, or quality of things,
Is called an *Adjective*; as, *bright*, or *round*, or *softest* wings.

A word that tells how things are done, as *quickly*, *bravely*,
well.
Is called an *Adverb*; and I'm sure you many more can tell.

A word that's used in place of nouns, a *Pronoun* we may call;
As, *I* for mother; *you*, for James; *this*, *that*, for hoop or ball

A *Preposition's* placed before a noun, and serves to show
Relation to some other word; as, Rover's *in* the snow.

And then *Conjunctions* join two words or sentences together;
As, man *and* boy, or birds will fly *and* winds blow o'er the
heather.

Then *Interjections*, *Oh!* and *Ah! Behold!* and many another,
Express surprise, delight; dismay, far more than every other.
{126}
And these the *Parts of Speech* we call; *Eight* parts as you may

62

tell;
  And all the language you will know, when these you've studied well.

NUMBER AND GENDER.

A NOUN or name that means but one,
  Is called in the *singular number*;
But when it stands for more than one,
  'Tis *plural*, child, remember.

* * * * *

A NOUN that is the name of males,
  As ox, or horse, or father,
Is *masculine* in *gender*, dear;
  While cow, and mare, and mother,
And all the names of females, child,
  Are *feminine*, 'tis true;
Now tell me all the names you know,
  And tell their gender, too.
But you will find there's many a noun
  Not male, nor female either,
As chair, and book; and such we call
  In *neuter gender*—neither.

{127}

ONE LITTLE CHICKEN.

ONE little chicken, two little chickens, three little chickens, dear;
  Don't you see we add *s*, when more than one is here?
  And this we do with almost all the nouns that may appear.

One little birdy, two little birdies, three little birdies soar;
  The *y* is changed to *i-e-s* for birdies two or more;
  And this, when a word shall end in *y* with a *consonant* before.

One little donkey, two little donkeys, three little donkeys
bray.
But here the *y* remains unchanged, and *s* is called in play;
And this, when a word shall end in *y*,where a *vowel* leads the
way.

{128}

LETTERS.

A, E, I, O, U,
   The *vowels* we may call;
W, Y, are vowels too,
   Whene'er they chance to fall
To the end of syllable or word.
   And this we well may know
That all the rest are *consonants;*
   Just nineteen in a row.

K, P, and T are called the *mutes,*
   Because they interrupt
All voice or sound; while B and D
   Can only intercept;
Hence these are partial mutes, my child;
   And H is *aspirate;*
And *th*, too, in *think* and *throne*,
   But vocal in *this, that.*   {129}
Then lip-letters, or *labials*,
   And *dentals*, or tooth letters,
With *palatals* and *sibilants*   Seem wondrously like fetters.
But, ah! instead of prisoning,
   They open wide the way

That leads to Learning's loftiest heights;
   Press on, and win the day.

* * * * *

WORDS.

TELL me the name of something, dear;
   As book, or ball, or kite;
Now tell some quality of each,
   As big, or round, or light.
And now some word that means *to be*   Yes, *is*, my child, you're
right.

The ink is black, The snow is white,
   The ice is hard—is cold:
The sky is blue, The air is light,
   Sometimes the child is bold.   {130}   And thus let names of everything
   Afar or near be told;
And Qualities of each and all
   Let memory infold.

* * * * *

NOW give one name, and tell me all
  Its qualities as well;
As, coal is black, and coal is hard,
  And coal's inflammable.

And now, you children should be taught
  That we need not repeat
The name, with every word that tells
  Its qualities complete.

Coal's black, hard, and inflammable,
  We say; but all so fast,
A comma follows after each,
  With *and* before the last.

And now use iron, chalk, and clay,
  Use water, snow, and ice,
Use thread and needle, pin and pen,
  Use every word that's nice.—

{131}

ANOTHER lesson now attend—
  We'll find some quality
Embraced by several different things,
  As you will plainly see.

Snow is cold, ice is cold,
  Salt is cold as well;
Snow, ice, and salt are cold, my child,
  As every one can tell.

* * * * *

A SMILE.

"SHE smiled on me, she smiled on me!"
  In ecstacy exclaimed
A little waif in tattered gown,

With form so halt and maimed.
Remember, even a smile may cheer,
  A cup of water, bless;
A kindly word, sow seeds of joy,
  Whose fruit is happiness.

{132}

TWINKLE, TWINKLE.

"Twinkle, twinkle, little star,
Up above the world so far,
Whisper now and tell me, pray,
What you are, and how you stay."

"Some of us away so far,
Planets like your own Earth, are;
And we shine with borrowed light,
Borrowed from the Sun, so bright.

"Some of us are silvery moons,
Shining all the nightly noons;
Some of us are jelly, soft,
Shooting, falling, from aloft.

{133}

Some of us are Nebulae,—
Faint and misty stars we be;—
Some are Suns to other worlds;

67

Here and there a Comet whirls.

"Having each our time and place,
Swinging in the wondrous space;
Held in line by Him who planned,
And who holds you in His hand."

{134}

OLD SOL IN A JINGLE.

Hi-diddle-diddle,
  The Sun's in the middle,
And planets around him so grand,
  Are swinging in space,
  Held forever in place,
In the Zodiac girdle or band.

  Hi-diddle-diddle,
  The Sun's in the middle,
And Mercury's next to the Sun
  While Venus, so bright,
  Seen at morning or night,
Comes *Second*, to join in the fun.

  Hi-diddle-diddle,
  The Sun's in the middle,
And *Third* in the group is our Earth;
  While Mars with his fire,
  So warlike and dire,
Swings around to be counted the *Fourth*.

{135}

{136}

```
Hi-diddle-diddle,
  The Sun's in the middle,
While Jupiter's next after Mars,—
  And his four moons at night

  Show the speed of the light;
Next golden-ringed Saturn appears,

Hi-diddle-diddle,
  The Sun's in the middle,
After Saturn comes Uranus far;—
  And his antics so queer,
  Led Astronomers near
To old Neptune, who drives the last car.
```

URANUS.　　　　NEPTUNE.

[Footnote: Other planets are as yet too little known to claim place.]

{137}

"ROBERT OF LINCOLN."

```
"Bob-o-link, bob-o-link, reed-bird,  butter-bird,
All through the country his jingle is gaily heard;
Reveling in rice-fields he sweeps through the South,
While wheat, corn, and barley-fields welcome him North,
And Bobby is wild with his singing and chatter,
So saucily calling with rattle and clatter,
```

Bob-o-link, bob-o-link, Tom-denny, Tom-denny,
Come-now-and-pay-me-that-two-shillings-one-penny,
No,-I'll-not-wait-for-a-day-nor-a-minute,
So-pay-me-up-quick-or-you'll-get-your-foot-in-it;—
Chink-a-chee, chink-a-chee, chink-a-chee, chin-it,
Yes,-pay-me-up-quick,-or-you'll-get-your-foot-in-it."

{138}

LIMPY-DIMPY-DINGLE.

Limpy-dimpy-dingle, chicky-bid would stray
To the trap that had been set for weasels, many a day,

Limpy-dimpy-dingle, chicky-bid walked in,
And the trap its teeth shut up, on chicky-biddy's shin.

Limpy-dimpy-dingle, chicky-bid is brought,
And her leg, so sore and big, we bathe with water hot.

Limpy-dimpy-dingle, here's a broken bone,
All so rough,—but close enough we bring the ends, right soon.
{139}
Limpy-dimpy-dingle, strips of paste-board cut,
We will place with care and grace, from thigh to trembling foot

Limpy-dimpy-dingle, softest cotton, too,
Just within the paste-board thin, to fit around so true.

Limpy-dimpy-dingle, now with tape or band,
Neatly wind, and closely bind, with deft and skillful hand.

Limpy-dimpy-dingle, nature'll do the rest,
And soon will knit the bone to fit, as good as very best.

CASTLE WONDERFUL.

I know a castle, curious,
  Of lovely form and make;
That we may view the castle through,
  A hasty peep we'll take.   {141}
The framework of my castle proud,
  Is neither wood nor stone,
But earthy matter mixed with lime
  And hardened into bone.

This frame, of oddments is composed,—
  In mind, the number fix,—
Of long and short and thick and thin,

Two hundred just, and six.

And these are fastened each to each,
  By hinges, like, or joints,
Which, with an oil so soft and pure,
  The Builder wise, anoints.

For garnishing this goodly frame,
  Quaint cushions, large and small,
Are fitly fashioned, each in place,
  And pliant, one and all.

For cushion covers, deftly wrought,
  A scarf so beautiful,
So pinkish-white, so loose yet tight,
  So warm and yet so cool;

Upon the smoothly rounded roof
  Is strewn the finest floss,
A filmy veil, as soft as silk,—
  Or is it fairy moss?   {142}
Two windows hath this castle fair,
  That shut and open wide,
With cords and pulleys, curtains fringed,
  And fixtures fine beside.

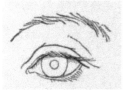

These wondrous windows even smile
  And speak and fairly dance,
And play at anger, hate, and love,
  And mischief, too, perchance.

These windows, too, are marvelous
  In that they let the light
Both in and out for him who dwells
  Within, the lordly knight.

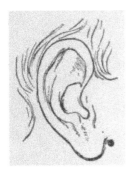

Two telephones of wondrous make,—
  A door, with guards and bell,—
A ventilator, double-bored,
  Aye does its duty well.   {143}
And ah! within, this castle grand,
  Is fitted to a T,
With everything that's needful there
  For serving you or me.

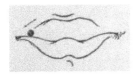

And strange to tell, this castle builds
  Itself, if but supplies
Be placed within the open door,
  With watchful care and wise.   {144}
It clears itself too of the dust
  And ashes strewed within,
If but the alley-ways are free,
  And outlets all a-kin.

And stranger still, this castle comes
  And goes where'er the will
Of him who holds the rule within
  Shall bid, his hest to fill.

And wondrous more than all beside,
  This house the temple is,
Of Him the great designer, God,—
  And "all the earth is his."

{145}

Now list, and of this castle grand
  A further tale we'll tell,
In language plain, so plain that all
  May read and heed it well.

The food we eat makes all our blood,
  And makes us children grow;
And if we eat improper food
  It harms from top to toe.

We all have teeth quite sharp and strong,
  With which to chew our food,
And in the mouth are glands and glands—
  Yes, quite a numerous brood.

These glands pour out saliva, free,
  To moisten what we eat
And then a trap-door at the throat
  Performs a wondrous feat

In guiding all the food along
  Into the Esophagus,
And thence to stomach through a pass
  Called Cardiac Orifice.

And here 'tis mixed with Gastric Juice,
  And into chyme is churned
Then through the gateway, Pylorus,
  As wiser ones have learned.   {146}
'Tis in the Duodenum now,
  Where it is mixed with Bile,
And with the Pancreatic juice,
  Which changes it to Chyle.

This Chyle flows on, and all that's fit
  For nourishment and growth,
Is taken up by Lacteals,
  Or "tubes with many a mouth."

These lead to the Thoracic Duct,
  Which holds a spoonful large,
And from this Duct a pipe proceeds
  Through which it may discharge.

Into the great Sub-clavian vein,
  Which to the Heart doth lead,
Whence it is sent into the Lungs,
  And into good blood made.

Then back into the Heart it flows,
    The muscles there contract,
And pump it into Arteries,
    Which wind to every part.

We'd like to tell about the Bones,
    The Ribs and Vertebras,
The Clavicle, or Collar-bone,
    Breast-bone, and Scapulae;   {147}
Of hinge, and ball-and-socket joints;
    Of muscles, tendons, skin,
Of lungs and veins and arteries,
    Of nerves and heart and brain.

But, Ah! we should your patience tire,
    Were we the whole to tell,
So, waiting till another time,
    We bid you now, farewell.

{148}

THE RATTLE OF THE BONES.

How many bones in the human face?
FOURTEEN, when they're all in place.

How many bones in the human head?
EIGHT, my child, as I've often said.

How many bones in the human ear?
THREE in each; and they help to hear.

[Footnote: Standard authorities give three, though latest works say four.]

How many bones in the human spine?
TWENTY-SIX; like a climbing vine.

How many bones of the human chest?
TWENTY-FOUR ribs and TWO of the rest.

How many bones the shoulders, bind?
Two in *each*; one before, one behind.

How many bones in the human arm?
In *each* arm, ONE; TWO in *each* fore-arm.

{149}

{150}

How many bones in the human wrist?
EIGHT in *each*, if none are missed.

How many bones in the palm of the hand?
FIVE in *each*, with many a band.

{151}

How many bones in the fingers ten?
TWENTY-EIGHT, and by joints they bend.

How many bones in the human hip?
ONE in *each*; like a dish they dip.

How many bones in the human thigh?
ONE in *each*, and deep they lie.

How many bones in the human knees?
ONE in *each*, the knee-pan, please.

How many bones in the leg from knee?
Two in *each*, we can plainly see.

How many bones in the ankle strong?
SEVEN in *each*, but none are long.   {152}
How many bones in the ball of the foot?
FIVE in *each*; as in palms were put.

How many bones in the toes half-a-score?
TWENTY-EIGHT, and there are no more.

And now, all together, these many bones, fix,
And they count in the body TWO HUNDRED and Six.

And then we have, in the human mouth,
Of upper and under, THIRTY-TWO TEETH.

And we now and then have a bone, I should think
That forms on a joint, or to fill up a chink.

A Sesamoid bone, or a Wormian, we call,
And now we may rest, for we've told them all.

{153}
WHOLLY HOLE-Y.

SEVEN million little openings,
   God has made upon your skin;
Mouths of tiny little sewers
   That run everywhere, within.
And along these numerous sewers
   All impurities must go,
That are not by other outlets,
   Carried off with active flow.   {154}
When these many little openings.
   We call PORES, get shut quite close,
Through your frame the poison wanders,
   Making you feel dull and cross.
It will make your lungs grow tender,
   And they'll soon be sore, and cough;
It will make your stomach feeble,
   And your head ache hard enough.

Then your heart can not be joyous,
   And your other organs, too,
Will get weak, and be unable
   For the work they ought to do;
Quaking nerves will groan and quiver,
   Weary bones be racked with pain,
And you'll all the time be saying:
   "How can I be well again?"

HEAT and BATHING widely open
   All the pores, when discords dire,
Quick flow out in perspiration,
   Quenching all the fever-fire.
Raveling out the tangled tissues,
   Setting free the life-blood's flow,
Pouring forth the pent-up poisons,
   Wakening thus a healthful glow.

{155}

{156}

THE BREATH O' LIFE.

Our lungs are formed of curious cells,
  And tubes to draw in air,—
And if we breathe quite deep and full
  And take our needful share,
'Twill keep our blood so red and pure,
  Our health so firm and true,
We scarce shall know what suffering means,
  But joyous feel, and new.

But if we wear our clothing tight,
   The little cells will close,
And then they cannot do their work,
   And thus our health we lose;
Or if we breathe the air impure,
   'T will give us tainted blood,
While plenty, pure, sun-ripened air
   Will make us glad and good.

{157}

THE GIRLS.

Three little girls with their sun-bonnets on,
   Wandered out for a walk in the dew;
And they tip-toed about, full of frolic and fun,
   While their aprons around them they drew.

But their little wet feet brought fever and cough,
   And their little red lips grew so thin;
And their little round faces were haggard enough,
   O, I'm sure they'll not do it again!

Not do it, I mean, without boots that shall guard
   Their ankles and feet from the wet;
For the care of the health brings a joyous reward,
   The neglect, brings us pain and regret.

{158}

THE TEMPERANCE CHILD.

Mamma, if you'd have me
  Be a temperance child,
You must give me only
  Food that's pure and mild.
Highly-seasoned dishes
  Make the stomach crave
Stronger things; and often
  Lead to drunkard's grave.

{159}

LISTEN, CHILDREN!

Listen, children! when your head aches,
  Do not eat, but wait a meal;
This will oftentimes relieve you,
  Making you right joyous feel.

Listen, children! when your stomach
  Rolls and tumbles, wait awhile;
Do not eat, but drink warm water,
  And you'll soon be glad and smile.

Listen, children! in hot water
  Put your feet when you've "a cold;"
Into bed now, wrapped in blankets,
  And you'll soon be well, we're told.

Listen, children! perspiration
  Is a saving from much sin:
Wash and rub, and dry well after;
  Thus we quell disease within.

Listen, children! when you're hungry
  Do not stuff you like a pig,
But eat slowly and chew thorough,
  Lest your teeth your grave shall dig.

{160}

TICK-TOOK, TICK-TOCK.

Tick-tock, tick-tock,
Sings the pretty cuckoo clock;
  Tick-tack, tick-tack,
Time flies on, but ne'er comes back.

  Tick-tock, tick-tock,
Sings the dainty crystal clock;
  Tick-tack, Tick-tack,
Work and wait, and never lack.

  Tick-tock, Tick-tock,
Sings the old grandfather's clock,
  Tick-tack, tick-tack,
Take and keep, the better track.

{161}

CURIOUS TREES.

THE COW-TREE.

South America's soil
  Yields the towering Cow-tree,
With sweet milk in its cells
  For you or for me;
Its sap is the Milk,—
  Cut the tree and it flows;
Like leather its leaves,
  And its branches like bows.

{162}

THE SUGAR-PINE.

Then, too, my dear children,
  The sweet Sugar-pine,
On Pacific's wild coast,
  In our own soil we find;
Cut or scoop out the trunk,
  And the juices ooze forth,
And harden, for sugar,
  Like icicles, North.

* * * * *

THE BUTTER-TREE.

And, funny enough,
   There's a Butter-tree, too;
Its seeds, when boiled down,
   Will make butter for you.
In India and Africa
   The Butter-tree grows,
With coffee and spices,
   As every one knows.

{163}

THE BREAD-FRUIT TREE,

And listen, dear children,
   In hot countries too,
The Bread-fruit tree grows,
   Most delicious for you;
Its great roasted nuts,
   Like soft, sweet loaves of bread,
Form most of the food
   On which natives are fed. {164}
And further, its fibres
   Of bark, will make cloth;
Its wood, boats and houses;—
   Its leaves are not loath
To be used for a towel,
   A table-cloth, napkin;
Its juice will make bird-lime,
   And tinder, its catkin.

THE CLOVE-TREE.

And, children, one more,
  Here's a spicy Clove-tree,
Growing forty feet high,
  Ornamental, you see;
The little round drop,
  Fixed the four prongs between,
Forms the blossom or flower,
  When it's not picked too green.

Now list, while I tell you,
  Clove-trees will not grow
Except in hot climates,
  Moluccas, or so,   {165} Where they bloom the year round,
  In the sunshine or storm,
With their trunks straight and smooth,
  And their pyramid form.

And lastly, dear children,
  Clove-trees never flower
Till a half-dozen years
  They have grown, maybe more;
Then the buds, picked by hand,
  And dried quickly, are best;—
Trees a hundred years old
  Often yield with the rest.

THE "TREE VILLAGE."

In the Solomon Group in the great Southern Sea,
  And on Isabel Island alone,
A tree village is found, up the steep, rocky ground,
  On the top of a mountain of stone.

So gigantic the trees that it is not with ease
  That the houses of natives are built,
For the stems are six score of our feet, maybe more,
  And you'd think they must live on a stilt.

By a ladder facade the ascent must be made,
  Formed of pliable trees, or a creeper
Resembling the vine, which the natives entwine,—
  And the ladder's drawn up by the sleeper;

For these houses are made but to sleep in, 'tis said,
  When some enemy threatens;—to guard
'Gainst surprise in the night, they are fortified quite,
  With great stones, to be thrown at a pard.

At the foot, of these trees are the day-huts for ease

And for eating and dancing and play,
Yet the huts up so high have a goodly supply
Of the needful for night or for day.

{168}

NO EYES.

Those Creatures that live in the dark,
   And have no use for eyes,
Are made without these organs bright,
   Which we so highly prize.

The fish in the Mammoth cave,—
   Some species of the Ant,
Have only a trace where eyes should be,
   Yet never know the want.   {169}
Who knows but girls and boys,
   Kept always in the dark,
Might come to have but little sight,
   And finally not a spark.

God meant us to live in the light,
   He has poured it all about;
Oh, let us not ourselves destroy,
   By shutting His sunshine out.

THE MAMMOTH CAVE.

"WHAT is the Mammoth Cave?"
  I hear the Children say,
Where fishes have no eyes nor sight,
  And where 'tis dark by day?

You all have seen a ledge
  Of big rocks piled, or stone?—
Now just suppose a door-way made,
  Or entrance to go in.   {171}
And when you're in, a path
  Leads on, right under ground,
And by-and-by you come to a place
  Like a room with walls around.

'Tis jagged and rough and rude,
  'Tis dark and damp as a grave,
But whether 'tis large or small,
  'Tis always called a cave.

Now, Mammoth means *monstrous big*,
  And the Mammoth cave, we claim
As the largest known in the world,
  And that's what gives the name.

And it has many a room,
  Quite large and wondrous grand,
And it has springs and streams and lakes,
  All dark, you understand.

And here are fishes, too,
  Yes, fishes with no eyes,
That have lived in the dark for ages past,
  As learned men surmise.

{172}

THE CAMELS.

The Camels live in desert lands;
Their feet are made to walk on sands;
They carry burdens far and near,
Where neither grass nor trees appear;

Where there's no rain, no rivers, brooks,
No water anywhere for folks;—
But God has made in Camels' chest
Peculiar sacs, for He knew best

What they must do, and that they'd die,
If He did not their drink supply.
Before they start they drink and drink,
Till every sac is full, I think;—

And at the mouth of every sac,
A muscle strong, but loose and slack,
Will tighten up when it is filled,
So that no drink can e'er be spilled.

And when on journey, last or first,
The camel wants to slake his thirst,
A bag-string loosens, and out-pours
Enough to satisfy for hours.

{173}

{174}

The laden camels, in a row,
Are called a Caravan, you know;—
Sometimes a caravan is lost,
Being buried deep in sand and dust.

A storm of wind, a Simoon named,
Will sweep across the desert sand,
When camels, men, and every one
Must throw themselves their knees upon,

And bury faces in the earth,
For thus alone they save their breath;
A fearful thing, but 'tis the best
That they can do,—now hear the rest.

{175}

Sometimes they're buried deep, and find
When they dig out they're almost blind
And cannot tell which way to go,
And thus are lost, a serious woe!

88

Sometimes, when lost, the drink for men
Gets short; is gone; they thirst, and then
They kill a camel just for lack
Of what he carries in his sac.

{176}

In deserts bare and bleak and drear,
The sun shines hot through all the year,
But many an Oasis is found,
Or spot where grass and trees abound.

And here is drink, and here they rest,
And take their fill of what is best;
Then travel on in thankful mood,
With song and shout! "Allah is good!"

{177}

KEY-NOTES.

L   M   N   R

LIGHTLY flowing LIQUIDS, we,—
   Tethered with our brothers.
Make we music, melody,
   More than all the others;
Lulling, mellowy, nimble, rare,
   Reveling in rhythm,
Running here and everywhere,
   Make me merry with 'em.

{178}

THE BEARS.

Wild bears are found all over,
   From Northern lands to South,

But largest, strongest, where 'tis cold
  And fiercest farthest North.

All bears are fond of honey,
  Of berries, too, and roots;
They hug or squeeze their prey to death,
  As this their nature suits.

They mate in June-y weather;
  Their little ones are cubs;
They sadly mourn when mates are killed,
  You'd almost hear their sobs.

They'll try to feed a cub
  That's lying cold and dead,
And will not flee, but stand and take
  The fatal knife instead.

{179}

{180}

They sleep through winter-time,
  But prowl in wildest storms,
With hope to find some creature killed,
  Or struck with death's alarms.

The bears are white, or black,
  Or brown or grizzly gray,
The white 'mong polar snows are found,
  Where half the year is day.

Their fur is used for robes,
  For coats, sometimes a muff,—
Their meat is prized by some as food,
  While some would call it "stuff."   {181}
They nimbly climb a tree,
  But "back down," for their frame
Is made so lungs would forward press,

90

If they head-foremost, came.

THE BEAR A BLESSING.

To people of Kamtschatka,
  The bear a blessing proves;
His skin forms beds and coverlets,
  And bonnets, shoes, and gloves.

His flesh and fat are dainties,
  And of his intestine,
Is made a mask for warding off
  The glare of Sun in Spring.

{182}

'Tis also used for windows,
  As substitute for glass;
Of shoulder-blade a tool is made,
  That's used for cutting grass.

Norwegians think the Bear is
  More sensible than men;
While Laplands call him "Dog of God,"
  And dare not him offend.

FRUITS

The fruits of the orchard and garden
  Are beautiful, luscious and good,
Partake of them freely, dear children,
  But eat them at meals with your food.

{184}

THE RACCOON.

Come, child, and see our pet Raccoon,—
The Raccoons live in the woods, you know;
  But ours was caught,
  And caged, and brought
From old Virginia, long ago.

{185}

Oh, no, you need not be afraid.
See, he is fastened with a chain;
  For ropes enough
  He has gnawed off,
And he is hard to catch again.

He e'en will climb this ten-foot fence,
And, careless where his feet may strike,
  He tumbles, bang!
  And there will hang,
His rope being caught by vine or spike.

And once the rascal ran away;
Was gone for days, and maybe weeks ;
  When children came,
  And charging blame,
Said, "Your Raccoon has caught our chicks."

{186}

"He's on our roof a-making mouth,
And chatters when we would go near.
  We wish you'd come
  and take time home,
So that our chick need not fear."   {187}
So now he's chained; yet up he'll climb
The stake to which he's fastened tight,
  And mutter low,
  So pleading, Oh!
'T would make you sorry for him, quite.

Just see his nose, so pointed, sharp,—
His ears as keen as keen can be,—
  His eyes so bright,
  So full of light,
And see him leap right merrily!

His fur, you see, is yellowish gray,—
And he is nearly two feet long;
  He lives on roots,
  And nuts and fruits,
When he's his native woods among.

But here we give him bread and milk;
He never eats like dogs or lambs,
  But takes it up
  From out the cup
With his fore-foot, as we use hands.

{188}

You'd laugh to see him, I am sure;
Of strawberries, too, he's very fond;
  Will poke around
  Till he has found
Each one among the hulls out-thrown.

Then, too, he's fond of nice clean clothes,
Will spring for sheet hung out to dry;
  And children dressed
  In very best,
Are sure to please his dainty eye.

No matter where his feet have been,
He'll spring and plant them, little pest,
  On something white,
  And then will fight

To hold, and hide it in his nest.

* * * * *   {189}
You've "come again to see our Coon"?
Well, he is gone; he plagued us so,
   We sent the "Rac"
   To Central Park,
Where you can see him when you go.

Oh yes, they're glad to get him, there;
They have no clothes hung out to dry;
   And children aye
   Must stand away,
For there a keeper's always nigh.

* * * * *

A "Yes" and "No" are common, hard,
   But "yes'm," "no-sir," choice;—
Let none but sweet and gentle words
   Flow from your gift of voice.

{190}

THE BANK-SWALLOWS.

In a village of Bank-Swallows,
  You will find so many a nest,
"That you scarce can tell their number
  Nor which one of them is best."   {191}
In the sand-hill, see the openings,
  Round or oval odd-shaped, some,
Size and form depending often,
  On how loose the sand become.

When with their short bills they pecked it,
  Clinging fast with claws the while,
Till they made an open door-way
  Suiting them in size and style.

Once within, they peck and peck it,—
  Sometimes quite a yard or more,
While the nest is snugly builded,
  Farthest from the outer door.

But, so wise are they, this archway
  From the entrance to the nest,
Is inclining ever upward,
  That no rain within may rest.

So the pink-white eggs are laid there,
  Safe from harm, till baby-birds
Chirrup forth to take their places,
  'Mongst the self-sustaining herds.   {192}
Smallest of the swallow species,
  Homeliest, too, yet favorites dear,
For their graceful, airy movements,
  And their simple, social cheer.

Found are they from North to South-land,
　Known of every tribe and race;—
Swift in flight, yet swinging, swaying,
　Skimming low from place to place.

Parent-birds care less for young ones,
　Than do other swallow-kind;—
Push them off half-fledged and timid,
　Each his food and home to find.

Thus they, many a time, fall prey to
　Hawks and crows, their enemies;—
Even the nest sometimes is entered
　By the snakes and fleas and flies.

Swallows migrate in the Winter,
　From the cold to warmer climes,
Flying back as Spring approaches,
　To the haunts of former times.

{193}

"Ne'er one swallow makes a Summer,"
　Is a saying everywhere;—
But when swallows come in myriads,
　Blessed Summer-time is here.

{194}

THE MOCKING-BIRD.

The New World boasts the Mocking-bird
  And whether caged or free,
His wondrous voice pours forth in songs
  Of rarest melody.

His notes swell out and die away,
  As if a joyous soul
Were wrought to highest ecstacy,
  All music to control.

{195}

His native notes are bold and full,
  And then he'll imitate,
Till it would seem the feathered tribe
  Were all arrayed in state.

He'll whistle for the dog or cat,
  Will squeak like chicken, hurt,
And cluck and crow and bark and mew,

So comical and curt.

While blue-birds warble, swallows scream,
  Or hens will cackle clear.
In robin's song, the whip-poor-will
  Pours forth his plaint so near.   {196}
Canaries, hang-birds, nightingales,
  He echoes loud and long;
While they stand silent, mortified,
  He triumphs in his song.

THE BUSY BEES.

Why do the little busy bees
  So dearly love their queen,
And wait upon and pay respect,
  With watchful care and mien?

{197}

Because the queen lays all the eggs,
  And mothers all the young,

While every father-bee that's hatched
    Is nothing but a drone.

The working bees might all be queens,
    If cared for and well-fed
When they are in the larvae state,
    But they're half-starved instead,—

While those intended for young queens
    Are fattened overmuch,
And nursed and petted every hour,
    That they full growth may reach.

For every different kind of egg
    That makes the different bees,
A different kind of cell is made,
    The queen directing these.

For drones or males, six-sided cells,
    Quite neat, and smooth, and nice;
For working-bees a smaller cell,
    Uncouth, and rough, and coarse;

{198}

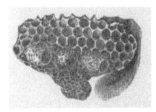

While those for queens are large and free,
    And fashioned fine with care,
And lined with softest, silken shreds
    So daintily they fare.

The queen-bee lays the worker-eggs,
    A dozen days, I ween,
And then the drones as many more,
    Then workers, then the queen.

Eggs, two or three, and sometimes four
    Are laid in worker-cell;
While drones and queens have each but one,

As oft is proven well.

The bluish eggs so close and warm,
   Hatch out with three days passed;   {199} When larvae,
white, as little worms,
   Are watched and fed and nursed.

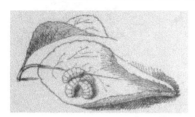

These larvae, when some six days old,
   Close in their cells are shut,
And there at once begin to weave
   A silken web about.

They turn and twist till all around
   Themselves 'tis woven quite,
And then they rest for twenty days,—
   'Tis such a pretty sight.

The small cocoons of working-bees,
   The larger ones of drones,
The large and plump and perfect ones
   Of all the coming queens.   {200}
In twenty days they now burst forth,
   Equipped from tip to toe,
The working-bees and drones, I mean,
   For queens come forth more slow.

The queen cocoons ope from behind,
   And I will tell you why,
'Tis that the reigning queen may sting
   The others till they die.

If mother queen leads off a swarm,
   A young queen they release,
And she may take another swarm,
   And leave the hive in peace.

Another queen is then let out,
  Perhaps a third and fourth,
As many as can raise a swarm,
  To follow them, not loath;

{201}

But when no more can swarm and go,
  Because not bees enough,
As I have said, the reigning queen
  Stings all the rest to death.

For in each hive and everywhere,
  One queen alone will reign,
And any interloper meets
  With sure and sharp disdain.

Of workers, some are strong to fly,
  While some are weak and small,
Unfitted quite, for load or flight,
  Or outside work at all.

These last complete the larvae-cells,
  And nurse and feed the young;
They mix the bee-bread, cleanse the hive,
  And care for every drone.

All bees have stings except the drones,
  And these, when Autumn nears,
Are stung to death with furious wrath,
  As by the book appears.   {202}
And now I hope you children all,
  Will use your wondrous power
To "gather honey all the day,
  From every opening flower."

{203}

```
BBB R YYY
B U YY
```

[Footnote: Bees are wises; Be you wise.]

{204}

HONEY-SWEET.

"Ah, but how do bees make honey?"
  Now the children, eager, ask;
And we'll try to give them answer,
  If we're able for the task.

See, the under-lip is lengthened,
  Like a trunk or proboscis,
Ending by a kind of button,
  Fringed with tiny moving hairs.

All along its length, too, fringes,
  Just the same, are growing forth;
And by means of these, the honey
  Is conveyed from flowers to mouth.

Then the bee has two small stomachs,
  In the first of which is stored
All the honey it can gather,
  But, when home, 'tis quick out-poured.   {206}
Bees have six legs; and in hindmost,
  There are baskets found, or bags,
Into which the pollen gathered,
  Is brushed off by the other legs.

And this pollen, for the bee-bread

And as food for young, they use,
  Mixed with honey and with water,—
  Swallowed and disgorged like juice

By the nurses, who digest it
  Partly, for the larvae-food,
Taking care that each shall have it,
  Just according to the brood.

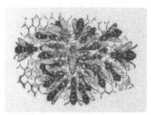

{207}

Now we'll watch and see them working;
  See them brush off pollen-dust;
See them, too, disgorge the honey,
  Into cells the sweetness thrust.

Children, with your useful fingers,
  Hands and arms and feet and head,
Do not let the bees surpass you,
  Making honey, nay, nor bread.

{208}

WHAT THEY SAY.

Those creatures that chew the cud,
  The "RUMINANTS" we call,
From "Rumen," or the stomach-pouch,
  In which their food doth fall.

A "SPECIES" is a kind
  Of animals or plants;—
Each species has a different name,
  And differing traits and wants,—

And species may unite
  To form a RACE we know,

For *race* from *root* is always drawn,
    And *roots* must spread and grow.

{209}

That men and women are
    The race most choice and fine,
We plainly see, and sometimes call,
    The *Human Race Divine*.

{210}

The noble Horse neighs out,
    "I am the race *Equine*,
And nearest seem, and dearest to
    The 'human race, divine.'"

The Ox and Cow l-o-o, l-o-o,
    "We are the race *Bovine*;
And we most useful are, unto
    The 'human race, divine.'"

{211}

The Ass and Mule bray out,
    "Our race is *Assinine*,
And very like us seem some of
    The 'human race, divine.'"

The Dog bow-wows as race
   Canine, Canine, Canine;   {212} While Tigers, Cats
and Catamounts,
   G-r-o-w-l, growl, as race *Feline*.

The Lion, king of beasts
   (Feline), roars "*Leonine;*"—
The Lamb that's to lie down with him,
   Ba-a, ba-as for race *Ovine*.

{213}

Fishes in lakes or seas
   or rivers Sport *Piscine;*
While birds in air or cages close,
   Sing, "race *Avine, Avine*."

All bees in hives or wild,
   Hum out the race *Apine;*   {214} And reptiles all
rejoicing crawl
   In race *Reptilian*.

* * * * *

I've a name that's made up of three letters alone,—
  That reads backwards and forwards the same;
I speak without sound,—yes, I talk without tongue.
  And to beauty I lay the first claim.

* * * * *

A word of three syllables, children, now find,
That holds the whole twenty-six letters combined. [1]

The B ing m t, John put some: [2]

stand	take	to	taking	
——	--	——	—	[3]
I	you	throw	my	

[Footnote 1: Alphabet]
[Footnote 2: The grate being empty, John put some coal on.]
[Footnote 3: I understand you undertake to overthrow my undertaking.]

{215}

BRITAIN'S RULERS.

Old Britain was under the Romans
  From fifty-five years before Christ (55 B. C.)
To four hundred fifty-five (455 A. D.)

Then her eight States on home-rule insist.   {216}
For many a year now they wrangle,
  Ah! yes, for quite three seventy-two,
Being ruled now by this king, now that one,
  As each might the former o'erthrow.

But ever since eight-twenty-seven (827),
  Britain's rulers have reigned by descent,
From Egbert, first "Monarch of England,"
  To Victoria, daughter of Kent.

A score reigned and fell.—Second Harold
  In ten-sixty-six (1066), proud; usurps,
But soon in fierce battle is conquered
  By William of Normandy's troops.

Then came William the Conqueror, a Norman,
  Then William the Second, his son;
Then Henry and Stephen and Henry,
  Then Richard (Coeur de Lion), and John.

Next Henry the Third, and First Edward,
  Edward Second and Third, Richard, two (II).
Henrys Fourth, Fifth and Sixth, and Fourth Edward
  Fifth Edward,—Third Richard, they rue.

Henry Seventh and Eighth, and Sixth Edward,
  Then Mary, Bess, James, and Charles First,—
Eleven years then with no monarch;
  Second Charles, Second James, not the worst.   {217}
Then William and Mary, then Anne,
  Four Georges, Fourth William, until
Came Victoria, long live her queenship,
  For she wields her proud scepter with skill.

OUR LAND.

A ship sailed over the blue, salt sea,
  For a man, Columbus called,
Had thought that the world was round, and he
  Of the old ideas had palled.

So, in fourteen hundred and ninety-two,
  He sailed across from Spain,
And found our continent so new—
  The "land beyond the main."   {219}
But jealousies and rivalries

And bickerings begun,
And Christopher Columbus now
    With grief was overborne.

Americus Vespucius soon
    Our shores came sailing round,
And stole the naming of the land
    Columbus sought and found;

While he, Columbus, lay in chains,
    And died in sore distress;
Yet won for us who tread his land,
    A lasting blessedness.

*   *   *   *   *

Young I-know is saucy and pert,
    And thinks himself wondrously wise;
But I-know, the second, steps in all so curt,
    And you'd think that each might lose his eyes.

{220}

SIGNS OF THE ZODIAC.

THE annual path of the Sun,
    The *Ecliptic* is called, as we see,—
And a belt, eight degrees, on each side,
    The *Zodiac* ever will be.

The principal planets all seem
    To move in the zodiac lines,
While the belt, of itself, is cut up
    Into twelve equal parts, called the *Signs*.

And these signs were first named, we are told,
    From their fancied resemblance to beasts,
Which astronomers thought they could see
    In the stars, from the West to the East.

{221}

There is Aries, the Ram, then the Bull,
  Which is Taurus,—then Gemini, Twins;
Then Cancer, a Crab and then Leo,
  A Lion, and Virgo, Virgin.

Next Libra, the Balance or Scales,
  And Scorpio, a Scorpion (with sting),—
Sagittarius, the Archer or Arrow,—
  Capricornus, a Goat's horn we bring.

{222}

Aquarius, the Bearer of Water,—
  And Pisces, or Fish from the sea,—
All together make twelve, and a wonder
  It is, that these fancies should be.

{223}

GRAPHO.

Children, you ought to know
  That *Grapho* can but mean
To picture out, or tell about,
  Some object or some thing.

Now *Geo* means the *earth;*

And so Geography
Means picturing out or telling about
  This earth of ours, you see.

As *Phono* means a *sound*,
  Phonography so terse,
Just pictures out or tells about
  The sounds of the human voice.   {224}
As *Photo* means the *light*,
  Photography must mean
A picturing of the light that falls
  Upon a thing, I ween.

Now *Astro* means the *stars*;
  And hence Astrography
Means to describe or tell about
  The stars we all may see.

And then Astronomy
  Tells all the various laws
That govern or relate to stars;
  Of their motions tells the cause.

Now *Bios* means a *life*;
  And so Biography
Means writing out the life of one,
  Which we may often see.

Zoos means *animal*;
  And your Zoography
Describes the animals that live
  On land or in the sea.   {225}
Then there's Stenography,
  A writing narrow, small,
Or, as so many call it now,
  "Short-hand," which tells it all.

And then Xylography—
  Engraving upon wood;
And Crystallography as well,
  That tells of crystals good.

But these are *ographies*   Enough for now, you think;
Yet when you're older, wiser grown,
  You many more will link.

{226}

THE STOP FAMILY.

"I'm a dot with a quirk," whispers little Miss Comma,
  "And you'll please not to pause long for me."
"I'm a dot over Comma," says Miss Semicolon,
  "And you'll pause twice as long where I be."

"I am dot over dot," Master Colon speaks out,
  "You'll pause longer for me than they say:"
"I am one dot alone," Period says with a tone
  That means: "Stop when you see me obey!"   {227}
"I'm a hook over dot," says Dame Interrogation,
  "I ask questions; but answer? O, nay!"
"I'm a splash over dot," says old Sir Exclamation;
  "I show wonder, delight, or dismay!"

"I'm a line east and west," says Miss Dash, "and I'm best
  At changing of subjects, you know."—
"I am Dash's small sister," says Hyphen, and kissed her;
  "I unite words, or syl-la-bles, so."

Then said Marks of Parenthesis (carefully curved),
  "We inclose what you well may omit;

But we're often displaced by Miss Dash (in your haste),
 Whom you sadly mistake for a wit."

Now Apostrophe, Caret, Quotation, exclaimed:
 "We are commas and hyphens combined;
We leave out, or put in, or reveal to your kin
 What you've said, when their backs you're behind."

Then Star, Daggers, Parallels, Paragraph too,
 Started up, staring wildly about,   {228} With "We
rise to explain on the margin, 'tis plain,
 Or to point a new paragraph out."

Of the whole Punctuation, each knew his own station.
 Each did his own duty, we see;
If we do ours as well, and of their's, too, can tell,
 We shall soon learn good readers to be.

* * * * *

"All is not gold that glitters;"
 Yet think not, children mine,
That all that glitters is not gold;
 The true must ring and shine.

{229}

LITTLE MISCHIEF.

Little Master Mischief
 Lives in Nellie's eye,
Sitting in the corner,
 Peeping out so sly;
Now he's crossed the snow-ground
 And in chamber blue,
Thinking he is hidden,
 Peek-a-boos at you.

Now he drops the curtain,
 Sure that he is hid,
But you see him dancing

Even on the lid.
Now, the curtains lifting,
   You can see he's crept
To the inner chamber,
   Where the love-light slept.

Watching now his moment
   He pops out, and see,
Mamma's spools and thimble
   Quickly disagree.

{230}

{231}

Shall we punish Mischief?
   Better teach the child
How to hold and lead him,
   Running now so wild.

Would she like her playthings
   Scattered here and there,
When she had arranged them?
   Would she think it fair?
Would she like her puzzle
   Portions of it, lost?

Would she like her dishes
  Everywhere uptossed?
Would she like her apron
  With a missing string,
Mamma hunting, meanwhile,
  Thread and everything?

Nellie, learn the lesson:
  Be to others true,
Always do as you would
  Have them do to you.   {232}
This the dear Lord's precept,—
  This the Golden Rule,—
This the highest lesson
  In our Nellie's school.

* * * * *

Be gentle and loving,
  Be kind and polite;
Be thoughtful for others,
  Be sure and do right.

{233}

GRANDMA'S CANARY.

Grandma loves her birdy,
  And when he gaily sings,
She will laugh and chat with him,
  At which he hops and springs.

Fearing though, that birdy
  Might not understand,
Grandma from the toy-shop,
  Brought a whistle grand.

Tuning now the whistle,
  To his sweet bird-note,
He in singing back to her,
  Nearly burst his throat,

{234}

Birdy, free outflying,
  Often comes to light
On Grandma's tip-of-finger
  Or chair-back, pretty sight!

From her hand she feeds him,
  And he oft will take
From her mouth the sugar,
  With a merry shake.

Yester-morn the window
  Being open wide,
Birdy thought it brighter
  On the outer side.

Grandma mourning sadly,
  Shed of tears a few,
Then she prayed the Father,
  "Show me what to do."

Soon she set his cage out
  On the window-sill,
Saying, "Birdy'll come now,
  Oh, I'm sure he will!"   {235}
Then she, hopeful, praying,
  "Bring my birdy home,"
Took the sweet bird-whistle,
  Playing "Birdy, come."

And the birdy hearing,
  Quickly came and lit
On the cage, and shortly
  Flitted into it.

Thankful now was Grandma,
  To the dear Lord, who,
Listening to her prayer
  Taught her what to do.

{236}

A BABY'S FAITH.

Our Maude was dancing with her doll,
    In childhood's chattering glee;
A brimming bucket standing by,
    The maiden failed to see,
And skipping, tripped; the bucket tipped;
    The water, cool and clear,   {237} Was rudely
swayed, but, undismayed,
    And quickly kneeling near,
Both little hands she spread above
    The water's merry surge.
"And what's she doing there," we ask?
    No answer, till we urge,
And then, "Why mamma, don't you know
    God stilled the waves so wild,
With His great hand? And so I thought,
    Although I'm but a child,
That I might still these little waves
    With my two hands so small;
And mamma, see, they're quiet now!
    But where's my baby-doll?"

* * * * *

HEALTH AND HAPPINESS.

Mamma keeps her children
    In the happiest mood
When she feeds them only
    With the simplest food.
Viands clog and pain them,
    Then they fret and cry,

And then when she whips them,
  Everything's awry.

{238}

THE MEADOW QUAILS.

Over in the meadow where the men make hay,
In an elm-tree shadow on a bright summer day,
Two speckled quails ponder as to what will be best,
Should the stout mower blunder on their pretty home-nest.

But a cloud in a minute from her great white bed
Threw a big silver bonnet o'er the sun's golden head
And the quails, though they wondered would their home be beset,
Cried aloud, and it thundered: "More wet! more wet!"   {239}
Then the great sturdy yeoman coming close to the nest,
With the heart of a true man beating soft in his breast,
Saw the parent-quails watching, with what fear who can tell?
Saw the baby-quails hatching, hardly out of the shell.

And who knows but he thought of his own precious baby
His dear little daughter in her mother's arms, maybe?
For he quickly made over that portion of meadow
With the sweetest of clover, and the softest of shadow.

To the quails who all summer lived alongside the lane,
Ever warning the farmer of the forth-coming rain;
For long ere it thundered and I hear the cry yet
They would call as they wandered, "More wet! More wet!"

* * * * *

DIDN'T-THINK is a heedless lad
  And never takes the prize:
Remember-well wins every time.
  For he is quick and wise.

{240}

THE LITTLE HOUSEWIFE.

This little girl knows how to make
A batch of bread, or loaf of cake;
She helps to cook potatoes, beets,
To boil or bake the fish and meats.
She knows to sweep and make a bed,
Can hem a handkerchief for Ned;
In short, a little housewife she,
As busy as the busy bee.   {241}
Let every girl learn how to do
All things that help to make life true;
That serve to keep the home-hearth bright;
That o'er life's burdens throw a light.
And then if she may never need
Herself to labor, she may lead
Her household in the better way,
That eft shall bring a brighter day.

The boys, too, let them learn to know
Of household duties, and to sew;
For oft a button, oft a rip,
By sewing they may save a "fip."
Yes, let them know that "woman's work"
With many a turn and many a quirk,
Is not "a play with straws," as some.
Would seem to think. 'Tis making home.

{242}

MOTHER-LOVE.

121

"AR-G-O-O, ar-g-o-o," is the song of songs,
  To the loving mother's ear;
"Ar-g-o-o, ar-g-o-o," these baby notes
  Fill all the house with cheer.

The baby's laugh, the baby's coo.
  The baby's every move,
Is music, joy, and grace to her,
  Who is rich in mother-love.   {243}
The precious pearl that is first unlocked
  By Nature's mystic key,
From out the baby's jewel-box,
  Makes mamma's jubilee.

The day of baby's mastership
  To raise himself upright,
An era marks along the way,
  By mother-love made light.

Her mother-voice lures on his step,
  Her care protects from harm;
While deeper into her heart he glides,
  With every opening charm.

And when he "ma-ma" sweetly says,
  Or "pa-pa," in her breast
His throne is fixed forevermore,
  This prince of babes confessed.

When threads of thought begin to spin,
  And webs of mind to weave,
When kindling soul looks out at eyes
  That know not to deceive,—

The mother's holiest task to keep
  Her darling pure and true;
Her constant care, her watchful prayer,

Alone can guide him through   {244}
The maze his youthful feet must tread,
   And if perchance he fall,
Her baby still in him she sees,
   Her love can cover it all.

O, the wondrous love the baby brings,
   Is far beyond our ken!
We only know that the fount once oped,
   Can never be dry again.

* * * * *

IT SNOWS! IT SNOWS!

It snows! yes, it snows! and the children are wild,
At thought of the fun in the snow-drifts up-piled;
The boy with his first new boots is in sight,
And the wee baby-girl, with her mittens so bright.
They are tramping and tossing the snow as they run,
And laughing and shouting, so brimful of fun;
While the ten-year-old twins, in a somersault mood,
Have measured their length from the barn to the wood.
A dozen times, yes, or it may be a score,
Till their cheeks are as red as the roses, and more;
Then the elfin of twelve and the boy of fifteen,
Are pelting each other with snowballs so keen,
That we, who are older, forget to be staid,   {245}   And
shout, each with each, as the youngsters, arrayed
   In feathery garments, press on or retreat,
   Determined to win, nor acknowledge defeat,
   And the snow tumbles down with such beauty and grace
   That the air seems filled up with soft, bridal-veil lace,
   Through whose meshes the sunbeams shall kiss Mother Earth,
   Till the buds and the blossoms are bred into birth.
But the children, at length, tired out with their play,
And stamping the snow from their feet by the way,
Come slipping and stumbling and scrambling along,
While the big brother catching the baby-girl's song,
"Oh, my finders are told!" gives her now a gay toss,
The golden hair streaming like distaff of floss;
And so cheery the group that is ranged round the board,
That for snow, blessed snow! we all thank the good Lord.

{246}

{247}

AN OLD SAW.

"If you'll break the first brake
  And will kill the first snake,
  You'll be sure to go through
  With what you undertake."

Thus our Grandma, quaint but queenly,
  Taught us grand-bairns one by one;
And the lesson relished keenly
  Filled each spring-time full of fun.

For the watchful eyes were eager,
  And the flying feet must roam
Till they every nook beleaguer
  Round the old ancestral home.

* * * * *

But 'twas not the broken brakelet
   That wrought good for after years;
Not the killing of the snakelet,
   But the conquering of fears,

And the patient, wistful watching,
   Educating thought and eye,
Made the brakelet and the snakelet
   Types of weal for bye and bye.

{248}

THE DANDELION BLOSSOM.

In the spring when the grass
   Had sprung up in the pass,
And the meadows with velvet were green,
   We children would tease,
   "O, dear mother, please
   Let us doff shoes and stockings,
   (Ah! naught gave us shockings),
And barefooted run o'er the leas,
Aye, barefooted run o'er the leas."

   And mother, so wise,
   Looking into our eyes,— {249} "There's a snowdrift down
under the hill!
   But when you will bring me,
   Yes, when you will fling me
   A dandelion blossom
   To wear on my bosom
You may barefooted run as you will,
Aye, barefooted run as you will."

   So for "guineas of gold,"
   O'er the dandelion-wold,
We hunted afar and anear;
   And with shouts of delight

We all greeted the sight
Of the fully-blown flower
Presaging the shower
Of bright blossoms that brought us such cheer,
Aye, the blossoms that brought us such cheer.

* * * * *

FEAR naught save that which slimes thee o'er
  With falsity or fraud:—
Let thine own soul stand clean and white
  Before its maker, God.

{250}

SUNSHINE.

The sun shines on forever
  Though clouds may hide his face;
His brightness and his glory
  The whole wide world may trace
For clouds are naught but vapor
  Whose fleecy veils unfold,
And softest silver lining
  We then with joy behold.

* * * * *

OUR ETHEL.

Our Ethel was not always,
  As people may have thought,
A goody-goody little girl
  Who never mischief wrought.

Oh, no, our darling Ethel,
  The precious little woman,
Although so very dear to us,
  Was most intensely human.

She waded into mischief
  Like ducklets into water,
And kept us ever on the watch
  With, "Daughter!" "Oh, my Daughter!"

{251}

She took the ribbon from her hair
    The kitten to bedeck,
Then brought its tail between its legs
    And tied it tail and neck.

She took her dolly to the pump
    And pinned it on the spout,
And then with all her might and main
    She pumped the water out.

"Oh, little Haynth tho' thelfith,'
    She cried, because her cousin   {252}   Besought one
pillow, while she hugged
    Them all, a half a dozen.

She found a bell that tinkled,
    And fastened it, for fun,
'Round kitty's neck then clapped her hands,
    And cried, run! Kitty, run!

She fain would pick the eyes out,
    Of little baby-brother,

"To find the pretty balls like those
    In fishes' eyes, and other."   {253}
And then she'd fold her little hands
    So quaintly and demurely,
You'd think she must be quite a saint,
    Or not a sinner, surely.

And thus her pranks from day to day
    And hour to hour repeated,
Would bring the thought, "Tis all for naught,
    Our aims are all defeated."

* * * * *

Nay, nay, not so, the years roll by,
    And Ethel's baby-mischief
Becomes the power that leads her kind,
    For by her force she is chief.

* * * * *

THE SIX SISTERS.

ONE of us e'er lives in dates,
One in every peach awaits;
One in pine-apple is found,
One in orange, bright and round,
One in plum, so luscious sweet,
And our last in strawberry—treat.

{254}

THE LITTLE GIRLS' LETTER TO GOD.

Now Susy's such a naughty dirl,
    And I ain't any better,
And so we thought we just would wite
    The dear dood Dod a letter.

And tell him all about our bad,
  Betause he'd have to know,
Or else he touldn't mate us dood,
  And so we told him how,

{255}

Once when I spit on Susy's dwess
  Then Susy spit on me;
And when I bwote her dolly's arm
  She smashed my Twistmas-twee.

Then when I pushed her off the wall,
  She spattered me with mud;
When I pulled up her tolumbine,
  She snapped my wed wose-bud

{256}

I talled her "old dwanmother Dwill"
  And she tailed me "old maid,"—
And then we stwatched each others' eyes

        Down in the darden shade.

And then my ma and Susy's ma
   Both said the only way
Would be to teep us little dirls
   Apart in all our play.   {257}
And so the bid, brown date was shut,
   And that was such a bother,—
'Tause Susy's yard was on one side
   And mine was on the other.

But we tould peet thwough all the twats,
   And tiss us thwough the hole
Where the bid, udly knot tame out,
   As bid as Susy's bowl,

For I love Susy awful much,
   And Susy she loves me,
And so we told the dear, dood Dod
   We'd twy dood dirls to be.

So now when we just feel the bad
   A-tomin' in our heart,
We both wun home and shut the date
   And teep ourselves apart.

And in a minute all the dood
   Tomes bat,—and then our plays
Seem nicer yet, and we fordet
   The naughty,—naughty—ways.

{258}

GRANDMA'S LESSONS.

"'Tis guilt to wear the garb of sin,
Though all be innocent within,"
These little girls heard grandma say,
And wondered if 'twere half in play.
But when they're wiser, older grown,
And when the world to them is known,
They'll learn to shun even seeming ill;
They'll learn with grace their lives to fill,
And thank dear grandma o'er and o'er,
For this, and many lessons more.
"'Tis guilt to wear the garb of sin,
Though all be innocent within."

"If you do well by others' ills,
You'll do right well," she said,
When we would come and tell about
The naughtiness of Ned.
"Now children, if you shun the bad
You may in others find,
And never let yourself be rude,
Or naughty, or unkind,
You'll learn to do by others' ills
Right well," dear grandma said,
"And in the way that's good and true,
Your youthful feet shall tread."

MY LITTLE FOUR-YEARS-OLD

Telling Dolly what she will say to her birthday friends

I'm four years old to-day, and I
Can talk enough for ten birth-days,
  And I shan't rhyme it, neither;—

For little girls can't do it nice.
No matter what they think, and so
   They needn't try, no, never.

I'm glad you all are here, and now,
With all our dollies in a row,
   I'm sure we'll have good times;
And when we have our apples, grapes,
And nuts and figs and patty-cakes,
   Who'll care for silly rhymes!

{261}

HANDSOME DICK.

ELZIE'S kitty, white as snow,
Loves his little mistress so,
That he'll come at her command,
Lift his paw to shake her hand,
Bow his head and kneel to her,
Rumpling all his milk-white fur;
Many another pretty trick,
Too, he's learned, our Elzie's Dick.   {262}
Well, the Church-Fair coming on,
Elzie thought, "What can be done
By a little girl like me,
In the cause of charity?"

Mam'a told her she would show
Her some fancy work to do,
Which a half-a-dozen dimes
Sure would bring;—so, many times
Elzie made her fingers fly
Neat and nice to form the "tie."
Now our Elzie, large and fine,
Looks like twelve, though only nine—
And the "tie" when quite complete,
Was so small, though choice and neat,
That it could not be denied,
Elzie was not satisfied.
So she shook her curly head,

As with curious smile she said:
"If I were a *little* girl,
Like Nannette or Cousin Pearl,
This wee 'tie' might then appear
Just the thing,—but now, I fear,
Looking at the 'tie' and me,
We shall seem to disagree.—

{263}

Now, Mamma, don't answer quick;
Stop and think,—my snowy Dick
At the Fair might win some pence,
By his wise obedience;
And his pretty winsome ways
Being shown through all the days;—
And, dear Mamma, then I should
Feel I'd done the best I could."

Quickly Mamma took the thought,
And a royal cage was brought;
Cushion made of scarlet bright,—
For our Dicky, pure and white,
Thus was wont to perch and sit,—
And a collar blue we fit
To his neck, when loyal, true,
He presents red, white, and blue.

So the cage is placed within
A sly corner, free from din,
And with tickets five cents each,
Elzie sought her end to reach.

{264}

"Handsome Dick! weight fifteen pounds"—
Whispers Elzie on her rounds;
"What is 'Handsome Dick'?" they say;
"Come and see, please,—step this way;"

And once seen they're glad to tell
Others of white Dick, as well;—
For the cat, as knowing now
He must make his courtliest bow.   {265}
Did his best to help along
Elzie's plan, the friends among.
Upon his cushion he would stand,
Or sit, as Elzie might command;
Then down upon his blanket lie
And be wrapped up like baby-bye;
Would lap his milk, or dainty, sip,
And shake his pretty under-lip,
Thus showing teeth as white as pearl,—
Then round and round would quickly whirl,
Till each one seeing, cheerful, said:
"For that five cents I'm sure we're paid."

Thus the three days passing by,
Which the Fair must occupy—
Dollars ten—ah, yes! and more,
Elzie holds within her store!
Dues for cage and tickets met,
And the *ten* is Elzie's yet,—
Which unto the Fair she gave
With an air so joyful-grave,

That it seemed a spirit bright,
Nestled in her heart so light;—
And a happier child than she,
We may never hope to see.

{266}

BESSIE'S KISSES.

Kisses, kisses, raining, raining,
  On her lips, her cheeks, her brow,
Till she, wearied, "Daughter, darling,
  Mamma's had enough for now."
"Ah! but Bessie has so many!"—
  Naught the pretty prattler daunts;
Mamma pleading, baby shouting,
  "Ah! but Bessie's more'n she wants."

{267}

THE DINNER-POT.

The homeliest things are highest worth,
  The dinner-pot's a treasure
Compared with diamonds, chains and rings,
  Which serve alone for pleasure;—

Enwreathe the dinner-pot with flame,
    And fill it with love's mixings,
And it possesses charms beyond
    All gold or fancy fixings.

And then, our bony frame-work, too,
    So stiff and hard and homely,
Will serve when plumpness all is gone,
    And lost is all that's comely.
Fling beauty, grace and sweetness round,
    Festoon your lives with flowers,
But ne'er forget that plainest things
    Are life's most precious dowers.

{268}

NANNY'S PLAY.

Our Nanny helped her mother
    In many a childish way,—
She picked up chips to feed the fire,
    And "played that it was play."

She loved the hens and chickens
    And fed them day by day,
And dubbed them each with quaintest name,
    And this was always play.

She hunted through the big barn
    For hens' nests in the hay,
And fetched the eggs right carefully,
    And this again was play.

She donned her mother's dust-cap
    And danced about so gay,
And planned how she would house-keep,
    And this was "truly play."

{269}

With basin full of water
  She scrubbed the door one day,
And splashed about till mother dear
  Must work instead of play.

{270}

With brush and broom a-sweeping
  She fluttered like a fay;
The broken cup soon told her
  'Twas anything but play.   {271}
She romped around the hay-field
  And shook the new-mown hay,
And with her baby-rake she gleaned
  The meadow for her play.

She ran to pick the berries
  That ripened by the way,
And with her basket full to brim
  This was the best of play.

So many things, so many,
  Far more than I can say,
Our Nanny in her childhood
  Has "played that it was play."

{272}
NANNY'S LESSONS.

Our Nanny was but four years old
  When mother said, "My love,
Your needle learn with skill to use,
  It will a blessing prove."

So Nanny learned to "overhand,"
  And "hem" so fine and neat,

137

To "backstitch," "run," and many a join
    That she could scarce repeat.   {273}
She learned to "catch-stitch" and to "cross,"
    To "patch" and "darn," as well,
To "gather," "plait," "box-plait" and "side,"
    To "feather-stitch" and "fell."

She sewed the buttons fast, and "worked
    The buttonholes" so neat,
That many an eld accomplishes
    With less success, the feat.

"Be sure your thread is smooth and strong,
    A goodly knot or two,
A double stitch for first, and then
    A fastening sure when through;

"And thus your seams will never rip,
    Your sewing never wear,—
Like buttons loose and hooks awry,—
    A slip-shod, shiftless air."

All this and more her mother taught,
    And Nanny conned it o'er
Till she was versed in all the arts
    That point the seamster's lore.

{274}

{275}

Her ninth birthday, and mother said
    "You're old enough to care
For all your clothing now, my child,
    Except the best you wear.

"And here, within this little chest,
    And in this drawer wide,
You'll keep them ranged so neat and nice,
    Whatever may betide.

"A place for this, a place for that,
    Each garment grouped aright,
That you may lay your little hand
    Upon it, day or night.

"No garment must be laid within,
    Except it ready be,
To don and wear, for thus you spare
    Us trouble, you and me."

And Nanny, pleased with mother's trust,
　　Accepted it with pride,
And, in her heart, the lessons learned
　　Forevermore abide.

{276}

NANNY'S RIDE.

Our Nanny oft in fancy
　　Soared up, the earth above,
And sailed the great air-ocean
　　With skylark or with dove.

And in this fashion musing,
　　One sunny summer's day,
Half-watching mother mending
　　And baby-brother play,

Without a word of warning
　　The old umbrella came,
Opened upside down before her,
　　And whispered soft her name.　{277}
"Come, Nanny you've been longing
　　For a ride, and now's your time:
Jump in,—be quick! And careful, too,
　　For I'm o'erpast my prime."

So, springing in, she sat there
　　As happy as you please,
And through the open window,
　　Was borne upon the breeze.

The sparrows eyed her keenly,
　　The doves left off their cooing,
And children, cause they couldn't go,
　　Set up a grand boo-hoo-ing.

She bobbed against a clothes-line,
    And all the wash went flying;   {278}   The good dame cried,
"A witch! a witch!
    The saints forefend my drying."

And next she got entangled
    In the telegraphic wires;
And when she jerked away from them,
    She bumped against the spires.

She hit the tallest chimneys,
    And set the smoke a-curling,
Then knocked a flag-pole all awry,
    The stars and stripes a-whirling.

Now, far beyond the city,
    With mountains in her face,
An eagle pounced to catch her,
    But she quickly won the race.

{279}

Within a mountain cavelet,
    Two baby-bears so young,
Smiled on her as she passed them,
    And greetings to her flung.

She heard the thunder rolling.
    And saw the lightning's glare,
From clouds away beneath her,
    While 'round her all was fair.

{280}

{281}

She met a cherub driving
    A brace of butterflies,

While dancing on a gorgeous one,
   Away in wonder-skies.

She saw an angel lighting
   The stars up one by one,
As he balanced on a cloudlet
   That was left behind the sun.

She heard angelic music,
   Far up, the blue along,
And knew 'twas Mary crooning o'er
   Her first sweet cradle-song.

{282}

She saw such wondrous pictures,
   So beautiful and grand,
Such skyscapes and such cloudscapes,
   Such waterscapes and land.

But now the fluttering insects
   All round her plainly told
That she was nearing Mother Earth
   Far o'er the daisy-wold;

And startled at the distance
   From home, the baby screaming
And mother still a-mending there,
   Told Nanny she'd been dreaming.

{283}

THE RACE.

A hop, a skip, and a gambol,
A run, a tumble, a scramble,
An up-and-a-going,
A laughing-and-crowing,
A weal-and-a-woe-ing,—
Yes, a race for a ball
Or a toy we may call,
This race that is human,—
For child, man, or woman,
Tis one and the same,
A mysterious game
That is played by us all,
And we each get a fall;
And so many it may be
That forever a baby
We feel in the race
For a name and a place.

OUR KENNETH.

Written for our pet, as indicative of what he *should be* but *is not*.

Know ye our little black-eyed boy?
  His name is Kenney Stone;
Now listen, for he always speaks
  In such a gentle tone.

He never says "I will!" "I wi'n't!"
  He's never rough nor rude,
But always bows with, "Thank you; please;"
  And tries to be so good.

Our Kenneth never kicks nor strikes,
  Nor makes an ugly face;
He never slides down banisters,
  Nor puts things out of place.

He never says a naughty word,
  Nor tells a big, big story!
O, no, nor even a little one,
  To make us all so sorry.

Our Kenneth is a gentleman,
  He will not scratch nor bite;
He never speaks to any child,
  A word that is not right.

Our Kenneth never slams the doors
  Nor stamps along the halls;
He goes away when he is told,
  And comes when mamma calls.

Our Kenneth, everybody loves,
  Because he's so polite,
Our darling little black-eyed boy,
  Our Kenney Stone so bright.

TO MY TEN-YEARS-OLD.

On thy cheek the roses lie;
　Lilies, on thy forehead fair;
Violets blue, in each bright eye,
　Sunbeams, in thy golden hair.

Pearls, within thy coral lips,
　Ears and nostrils, crystal-clear,
Dainty, sea-shell finger tips,
　Form, a sylph might love to wear.

Yet no beauty, thou, my child,

Save as filled with inward grace;
  Save a spirit, undefiled,
    Warm thy heart and wreathe thy face.

{288}

DARE TO SAY NO.

Dear children, you are sometimes led
  To sorrow, sin, and woe,   {289} Because you have
not courage quite,
  And dare not answer, No.

When playmates tell you this, or that
  Is "very nice to do,"
See first what mamma says, or if
  You think 'tis wrong, say No.

Be always gentle, but be firm.
  And wheresoe'er you go,
If you are asked to do what's wrong,
  Don't fear to answer, No.

False friends may laugh and sneer at you.
  Temptations round you flow,
But prove yourself both brave and true,
  And firmly tell them, No.

Sometimes a thing that's not a sin,

    You might be asked to do,—
But when you think it is not best,
    Don't yield, but answer, No.

True friends will honor you the more,
    Ah, yes, and false ones too,
When they have learned you're not afraid
    To stand and answer, No.   {290}
And when temptations rise within,
    And plead to "come," or "go,"
And do a wrong for "_just this once_"
    Be sure you answer, No.

For when you once have done a Wrong,
    The Right receives a blow,—
And Wrong will triumph easier now,
    So haste and answer, No.

There's many a little boy and girl,
    And man and woman too,
Have gone to ruin and to death
    For want of saying, No!

So, young or old, or great or small,
    Don't fail, whate'er you do,
To stand for Right and nobly dare
    To speak an honest No.

{291}

ASK MOTHER.

Yes, my darling, when you question,
  I will answer, simple, plain,
Just the Truth;—and when playmate
  Tells you anything again,
Come to Mother, she will tell you,
  Yes, and tell you always true,
For she knows what's low and sinful,
  And what's right and wrong for you.

TELL MOTHER.

'Tis wrong, my dear, to do a thing
  That mother must not know;
And when your playmates, old or young,
  Shall tell you thus to do,
Leave them at once, and quickly come
  To your dear Mother's side,
And tell her,—for she'll know what's wrong,
  And she will be your guide.

{292}

DON'T TELL A LIE.

Don't tell a lie, dear children,
  No matter what you do,—
Own up and be a hero,
  Right honest, brave, and true.

You'd better have a whipping
  Each day than tell a lie,—
No, not a "white one," even,
  They lead to blackest dye.

The rod but hurts your body,
  While lies deform your soul;—
Don't mind the present smarting,
  Keep the spirit pure and whole.

But I am sure that mamma
  And papa, too, will try
To help you children tell the Truth,
  Nor drive you to a lie.

They will not punish harshly,
  Nor when they're angry, quite;
Nor promise, and then fail to do,—
  But always lead you right.

{294}

LITTLE MOSES.

In the Talmud you will find it,—
  In the quaint and curious lore
Of the ancient priests, or Rabbins,
  Whom the people bowed before;

Find the story of an infant
  Sitting on the kingly knee;
"Little Moses," Pharaoh calls him,—
  Crowing loud in baby glee.   {295}
And the banqueters were cheering,
  When the infant with a spring,
Reached and caught the crown that rested
  Upon Pharaoh's head, as king.

Caught the crown, and quickly placed it
  On his own unwitting head;
But the king and all his princes,
  In the deed a meaning read.

Then spake Balaam, the magician,
  "Not because the child is young,
Hath he done this thing unknowing;—
  He hath mocked thee, he hath flung

"In thy face thy kindly dealings;
  Such hath ever been the way
Of his people; a usurper—
  Let his blood be spilled this day."

But the winsome baby-fingers
  Toying with the kingly beard,
Won the edict: "Call the judges;
  Let their counselings be heard."   {296}
So the judges and the wise men

Came with Jethro, Midian's priest,
Who, with wish to save young Moses,
    Thus his majesty addressed:

"If it to the king be pleasing,
    Fetch two plates, and we will hold
Them before the babe, a-brimming,
    One with fire, and one with gold.

"If the child shall grasp the golden,
    He hath done this knowingly;
He will trample on thy statutes;
    For thine honor he must die.

"But if he shall grasp the other,
    Know, O King, he knoweth nought
Of a royal crown or scepter,—
    And his life with fire is bought."

These wise words, the king approving,
    Plate of fire and plate of gold,
Courtiers brought, and screams of anguish,
    Soon the childish choosing told.   {297}
For he, baby-like, had thrust it
    In his mouth; and though he flung
Quick the coal, he ever after
    Spake with slow and stammering tongue.

[Footnote: Exodus IV:10]

* * * * *

Charming 'tis to see
Children who agree;
Chaste, and choice, and cheery,
Chiming in so merry,
Childlike, ever;
Churlish, never.
Championing the good;
Challenging the rude;
Chary as the dove;
Chief in Jesus' love.

{298}

THE CHILDREN'S RAILROAD.

Old Time has built a Railroad,
  On which you children speed
To a land of light and plenty,
  Or a land of darksome need;
And soon you'll come to a meadow,
  Where two tracks mark the way,
But they'll run close up alongside
  For many and many a day.

And one is strewn with roses,
    While one looks bleak and bare,
With now and then a berry-bush,
    And a violet here and there;—   {299}
On one you'll find companions
    Who but for pleasure seek,
While friends along the other,
    Will words of wisdom speak.

Be careful in your choosing,
    For if you take the *Right*,
You will travel in the shadow
    Of the Rock that shields at night;
'T will lead through greenest pastures
    Where softest brooklets flow,
And land you at a Station
    That is full of cheer and glow.   {300}
On the other track, the roses
    Are backed by sharpest thorns;
While berries always nourish,
    And the violet but adorns;—
You will stumble into sluices,

And what is worse than all,
Your self-respect and conscience
  Grow weak with every fall.

Yes, if you choose the other
  That looks so bright and gay,
You'll find the bridges broken,
  And the road-bed washed away;
And when you near the Station,
  You'll switch to a fearful leap,
That will hurl you into darkness,
  And bury you in the deep.

But those who choose the Right one
  Grow manly, womanly, true;
God's love-light shines upon them,
  And falls as heavenly dew;—
They grieve at your wild folly,
  And will gladly help you back,
If at any curve or turning
  You seek the trusty track.

{301}

But ah! the scars you're wearing,
  From thorns that pierced you sore,—   {302} And the ditches
in which you've fallen,

```
     That were strewn with roses o'er;—
And the joys you've lost, unnumbered,
   That spring from good deeds done;
And the fruits you've missed, unmeasured,
   That by others have been won.


Though friends may be indulgent,
   And loved ones even forget,
Yourself can never banish
   The memories that beset.
You will wish you had never traveled
   The way that leads to death;
You will wish you had never reveled
   In the viper's venomed breath.


So beware which track you follow;
   And again I say, beware!
The *False* is strewn with roses,—
   The *True* looks bleak and bare;
But this, 't is plain, is only
   That youthful, artless eyes
Are open to show and glamour,
   But see not deep nor wise,    {303}
To Truth then, children, listen,
   And cultivate the seed
That in your hearts God planted,
   To serve your every need;—
Yes, heed the voice within you,
   And follow it all the way,
For it will help you choose the road
   That leads to endless day.
```

{304}

THE PHOEBE'S NEST IN THE OLD WELL-WHEEL.

"Phoe-be, phoe-be," why, 'tis a little bird,
"Phoe-be, phoe-be," singing the pretty word;
"Phoe-be, phoe-be," brown feathers cover him,
Gray breast, with blackish stripes scattered all over him.

"Phoe-be, phoe-be," here comes his little mate,
"Phoe-be, phoe-be," both on the garden gate,
"Phoe-be, phoe-be," loving now they trill,
Planning to build a nest in the old well-wheel.

"Phoe-be, phoe-be," now the nest is begun;
"Phoe-be, phoe-be," now it is nearly done;
"Phoe-be, phoe-be," how will the birdies feel,
When the egg is dropped down, with turn of the wheel.

"Phoe-be, phoe-be," children are sorry now,
"Phoe-be, phoe-be," birds are all a-worry now,
"Phoe-be, phoe-be," laying eggs day by day,
While the turn of the wheel ever drops them away.   {305}
"Phoe-be, phoe-be," never the lesson learned,
"Phoe-be, phoe-be," year by year they returned,
"Phoe-be, phoe-be," building persistently,
Where the turn of the wheel dropped the eggs all away.

Phoe-be, phoe-be, yet not in vain you wrought,
Phoe-be, phoe-be, for, by your folly taught,
Phoe-be, phoe-be, children plan so to build,
That no eggs may be lost by the turn of life's wheel.

{306}

MABEL'S SNOW-FEATHERS.

153

Listen, children, while I tell you
    What our merry Mabel said
When she saw the feathery snow-flakes
    Tumbling down about her head.

Clapping hands and dancing gaily,
    "Mamma, mamma, come and see!
Come and see the feathers, mamma,
    Soft and white as they can be!"   {307}
Standing then a moment, pondering
    As it were, whence came the snow,
Little face so wise and thoughtful,
    Mabel cried: "Oh, now I know,

"There are lots of eider ducklets
    Up in Heaven, above the blue,
And they're dropping off their feathers,—
    And such downy feathers, too!

"See them frolic with each other;
    See them kiss as fast they fly;
See them make believe they are going to,
    Then go gaily flitting by.

"See them on the Spruce and Balsam,
    Pile up little soft, fat hands;
See their many plump, white cushions;
    See them wave their fairy wands.

"See the showers of flying feathers
    Whisking 'round in merry moods;
See, the telegraph their perch is,—
    Oh, I'm sure they're almost birds!"   {308}
Now she fancies she can hear them
    Whisper of their ducklet birth;—
Hear their soft and wean-y quacklings,
    As they tumble down to earth.

Now she listens for the jingle
  Of the sleigh-bells they will bring;
Now she sees the flying horses,
  Prancing gaily at their ring.

Lovely are these fleecy feathers,
  Dainty in each rare device;
All unlike our ducklet feathers,—
  White and soft, but cold as ice.

{309}

Yet they cover, warmly cover
  Mother Earth so bleak and brown;
Cover her with feathery mantles,
  Comforters of eider-down.

FOREST TREES.

Children, have you seen the budding
  Of the trees in valleys low?
Have you watched it creeping, creeping
  Up the mountain, soft and slow?
Weaving there a plush-like mantle,
  Brownish, grayish, red-dish green,
Changing, changing, daily, hourly,
  Till it smiles in emerald sheen?

Have you watched the shades so varied,
  From the graceful, little white birch,
Faint and tender, to the balsam's
  Evergreen, so dark and rich?
Have you seen the quaint mosaics
  Gracing all the mountain-sides,
Where they, mingling, intertwining,
  Sway like softest mid-air tides?   {311}
Have you seen the autumn frostings
  Spread on all the leafage bright,
Frostings of the rarest colors,

Red and yellow, dark and light?
Have you seen the glory painted
  On the mountain, valley, hill,
When the landscape all illumined,
  Blazons forth His taste and skill?

Have you seen the foliage dropping,
  Tender cling, as loth to leave
Mother-trees that taught them deftly,
  All their warp and woof to weave?
Have you seen the leafless branches
  Tossing wildly 'gainst the blue?
Have you seen the soft gray beauty
  Of their wintry garments' hue?

Have you thought the resurrection
  Seen in Nature year by year,
Is a symbol of our rising
  In a higher, holier sphere?
Children, ye are buds maturing;
  Make your autumn rich and grand,
That your winter be a passage
  Through the gates to Glory-land.

{312}

CHILDHOOD FANCIES.

The twilight gray is falling,
  Now list and you shall hear
The footsteps of the sylphid fays,—
  This is their hour of cheer.

List to the gentle patter
  On each wee blade of grass,
As it is bent, and back again,
  Whene'er the fairies pass.   {313}
Upon the tips of grasses

157

They cross the meadows, lawn,
And laugh and dance and play and sing,
  From twilight hour till dawn.

They light their myriad lanterns,
  And hang them in the arch
Of blue that canopies o'erhead,
  And by their light they march.

They sometimes miss a fairy,
  And take a lantern down
To search for her, and mortals say;
  "A fire-fly flits around."

On leaves they hang their diamonds,
  Their pearls in every flower;
Their gauzy veils upon the grass,
  They spread for fairy bower.

Their slender wings are hanging
  On every shrub, across;
Their seats are dainty cushion-beds
  Of green and springy moss.   {314}
Their shrubbery of coral
  Is gray and scarlet-tipped;
Their hair upon the maize is hung
  Each Summer, when 'tis clipped.

The mushroom forms their table,
  Their dishes, acorn cups;
The ant-hills are their barracks high;
  Their cannon, "hemlock pops."

Their scarfs of plush are lying
  On ripening grape and peach;
Their sea-shells 'neath the apple trees,
  Each Spring bestrew their beach.

They paint the leaves in Autumn;
  They make a tiny rink
Of every puddle, fen, and dike,
  And skate from nave to brink.

They brown the nuts in forests,
  The burrs they open wide;
They lure the feathers from the clouds.
  And pile them up, to slide.

{315}

They build along the way-side
  Their fairy palisades,—
The "hoar-frost" some have christened it,—
  And hold West Point parades.

They sketch upon the windows
  Such pictures as no power
Of man can ever execute,
  And on them pearl-dust shower.   {316}
All these and myriad fancies
  That never can be told,
My childhood days so new and sweet,
  In memory infold.

But mother softly whispers,
  "Tis not the Fays, my dears,
Tis old Dame Nature's song of songs,
  The 'Music of the Spheres.'

"List ever for it, children,
  Twill bring you close to God;
Each sound but echoes Him who made,
  Each motion is His nod."

* * * * *

  "Waste not, want not," be your motto,—
    Little things bring weal or woe;
Save the odds and ends, my children,
    Some one wants them, if not you.

{317}

LIZZIE AND THE ANGELS.

159

Little Lizzie, thoughtful, earnest,
    Springing up at break of day,
Thinks she heard the angels whisper
    Softly, as she knelt to pray.   {318}
"Yes, they whispered to me, mamma,
    And they told me lots of things,—
And they said, 'O Lizzie, Lizzie,
    'Tis your temper trouble brings!'

"Then they said: You, child, can never
    Be a woman good and true,
If you let your fiery temper
    And your own will govern you;
And they told me 'even Jesus
    Said, 'Thy will, not mine, be done,'
And that if I grew up wilful,
    All my life I can but mourn.

And they told me, too, dear mamma,
    That if I were called to die,
I could not be glad in heaven,
    For no heaven in me would lie.
Now, what shall I do, dear mamma,
    That I may be good and true?
How shall I my temper govern,
    And my wicked will subdue?"

"Lizzie, darling, if you listen,
    You will hear a voice within,   {319}   That will tell you
every moment,
    What is Right, and what is Sin.
But you must not disobey it,
    Or it will grow faint and weak;
You must watch to catch its whispers,
    Hurry when you hear it speak.

{320}

"For if you should linger waiting,
  There's another voice will say:
Never mind, nobody'll know it,

Even though you disobey.'
And this other voice, this Tempter,
   Sure will lead you to the wrong,
While the voice of the good angel
   Fills your life with cheer and song.

"In your play and in your working,
   You the Golden Rule must heed;
Do by others as you'd have them
   Do by you, if in their stead.
Better far to *bear* and *suffer*   Than to *do* a wrong, my child;
Better give up every pleasure,
   Than to be by sin beguiled.

"In your eating, in your drinking,
   In your clothing, in your talk,
You can glorify the Father,
   Or in wickedness can walk.
For your little body, Lizzie,
   God has said, 'Keep holy, pure,'   {321} Tis His 'temple' He
has lent you,
   Keep its every gate secure,

"What you eat and drink makes muscles,
   Bones and nerves, and brain, and thought;
And by food and drink improper,
   Fearful evils may be wrought.
Much of meat and spice and candies,
   Makes your blood impure, and then
All your body's in a jangle,
   And your temper's wild again.

"And your clothes if tight or heavy,
   Help to make your blood impure;
Help to make you weak and wicked,
   Into evil ways to lure.
Foul air, too, your blood will poison
   Sitting up too late at night;
All these things will make it harder
   For you, child, to do the right.

"Bad companions also lead you
   To the wrong, and tempt you sore
To defy the voice within you
   Till it, grieved, will speak no more,—   {322} Do not
hesitate to tell them
   You cannot their ways approve.
Do not yield to their enticements;
   Tell them 'No!' with firmness, love.

"Do not ever let a single

Word unkind, nor coarse, impure,
　　Pass your lips; for these will lead you
　　　Toward the bad, you may be sure.
Do not let a playmate tell you
　　Anything that must be kept
As a secret from your mother;—
　　Something's wrong, so don't accept.

"Always tell a thing precisely
　　As it is; don't try to make
It more fine and entertaining;
　　Tell the truth for Truth's dear sake.
Never lay a finger, darling,
　　On what is not quite your own,
Lest temptation overtake you,
　　And your honesty be gone.

"In the silence of your chamber,
　　When no human being's nigh,　　{323}　Don't forget that God
is with you,
　　Watching with all seeing-eye;
Don't forget that He will know it
　　If you do a thing that's wrong;
Keep yourself so pure and perfect,
　　That your life shall be His song.

"Now, dear child, the blessed Jesus
　　Always, when you wish it, hears,
Giving help to those who ask it,
　　Lightening woes, and lessening fears.
Follow always His example;
　　Take His precepts for your guide;
Learn to trust Him, for He's walking
　　Ever loving at your side."

{324}

CHILD-MEMORIES.

Was ever so sweet the clover,
  Was ever so clear the brook,
As my child-days, over and over,
  Found fresh in the dear home-nook?   {325}
Was ever such grace of motion,
  Or ever such trills of song.
As the birds in mid-air ocean,
  Poured childhood's plays among?

Were ever so bright the noondays,
  Were ever the skies so blue,
Or so soft the slanting moon-rays,
  As stole my childhood through?

Was ever so dear a mother,
  Or a child so sweet, I pray,
As my blue-eyed baby-brother,
  In the time so far away?

Was ever so true boy-lover,—
  O, ever such pictures bright,
As my child-days, over and over,
  Reflect by memory's light!

{326}

NELLY AND NED.

"I'M twelve years old to-day," says Ned,
  "And wish I were twelve more, sir,—

And Nelly Warner's almost twelve,
  So we'd be twenty-four, sir."

"'And what of that!' Why, Nelly 'n' I
  Have always played together;
And then I draw her on my sled,
  To school in stormy weather.

"And all the goodies that we get,
  We share them half and half, sir;
And O, we have such lots of fun,
  I'm sure 'twould make you laugh, sir!

"Now Nelly lives in Cottage Square,
  While I live 'round the corner,
And all the boys would laugh and shout,
  'Ned Jarrett loves Nell Warner.'

{327}

{328}

"I didn't care for this, you know,
  But O, I couldn't bear it

When they began to laugh at her,
  And say, 'Nell loves Ned Jarrett!'

"And so I thought I'd have to fight,—
  And though I was the smallest
Of all the party, I's so mad
  I'd easy beat the tallest.

"But Nelly coaxed and comforted,
  And said, 'Why would I do it,
When they had only told the truth,
  And everybody knew it!'"

{329}

THE CLAMBERERS.

All you babies
  Perched in air,
Careful how you
  Caper there!
Careful lest the
  Little feet
Or the little
  Hands so sweet,
Lose their hold
  And babies fall,—
Careful, careful,
  Babies all.

{330}

THE NEW WHITE JATTET.

I never seen such naughty dirls
  As Susy Jones and Ellen;
They laughed, O desht as hard's they tould
  When I twipped up and fell in
The old toal-hole. And see, mamma,
  I tore my new white jattet;
And when I twied, they laughed and laughed,
  And said, "O, what a wattet!"

166

The bid dirls talled them most untind,
  And said they surely knew it,
The teaching of the Dolden Wule,
  And then how tould they do it!
I duess they'd twy if they was me,
  I duess they'd mate a wattet,
If they should fall in a toal-hole,
  And tear their new white jattet.

{331}

REMEMBER THE POOR.

"SWEET, my darling, come and see
  What mamma has brought for thee;
Garments soft and ribbons bright,
  Hat and coat, a pretty sight;
Sweet, my child, what shall we do

With the old, now you've the new?"

"Why, mamma, this frock and frill,
　These are good and pretty still.
But as they are quite too small,
　Give them, please, to Lillie Ball
In the cottage by the hill,
　She'll be glad, I know she will;
For mamma, they're very poor,
　And 'tis cold to cross the moor
In their tattered garments few;
　Mamma, may I give the new?"

"No, my child, and yet you may
　Sometimes give new things away.
Keep your pennies, and they'll be
　Dollars, by and by, two, three;
Thus you now and then may have
　Something new and fresh to give."

{332}

THE LITTLE STREET-SWEEPER.

Look at that little girl sweeping the crossing;
See how the mud her bare legs is embossing!
And her feet are so slippered with mud, that it seems
As though from the ground she grew up 'mongst the teams;
And why she's not run over surely's a wonder,
Standing there sweeping, the horses' feet under.
See her close curls and her bright, beaming eye;
Though fearless, the glance, you perceive, is half shy,
{333}　As so lightly she swings her wet broom, and so true,—
Let us cross, and we'll give her a penny or two.

But wait, now a passer-by hands her a penny;

168

Just see her bright glance twinkle over to Benny,
The little hunchback sitting there on the curb-stone,
Close up to the lamp-post, that he may disturb none.
His crutches beside him a sorry tale tell;
But see, he's a basket of knick-nacks to sell;
And a lady has bought for her child a toy whip,
And now from her port-monaie gives him the scrip,
But refuses the change,—and with tears in his eyes,
He thanks her and blesses, with grateful surprise;—
And the glance the boy now flashes over to Jenny,
Is as bright as she gave him when she got the penny.
O, I've seen them so many times! always together,
Always happy and cheery, in bright or dull weather;
For though he makes the most when it's fair, as they show me,
Yet she does the best when it's muddy and stormy.

Watch, now, her quick smile of such pleased recognition:—
To win it I oft come this way on my mission.
But see, she draws back as I offer the penny,   {334} And
modestly says, "Madam, please keep the money,
For you know 'tis a pleasure to me to be sweeping
The path for you, lady;" and, all the time keeping
Her broom just before us to brush the least speck,
The sweet smiles in her eyes her whole being bedeck.
So I keep it, for she has as good claim as I
To the right to do favors and none will deny
That "It is more blessed to give than receive,"
And her sweep is far more than my pennies to give.
But we'll stop and see Benny, and make it up there,
For in all that each gets they will both have a share.
A nice little bib for my baby at home,—
A patent tape-measure, a mother-pearl comb;
And Benny's pale face lightens up with a glow
Such as angels rejoice in;—now, Maud, we must go.
But to Benny: "I'm thinking to-night I may come
And bring my friend with me, to see your new home."
"O, if you will!" says the child with delight
Rippling over his face like a sunbeam—and quite
As joyously, Jenny: "O, madam, please do,
For we've something at home that we want to show you!"

So when 'tis near night-fall we take the short car   {335}
That off through West Fourth Street goes winding afar,
And away to the Hudson, almost, we shall find
A lone-seeming tenement cuddled behind
Huge heaps of fresh lumber so piney and sweet,
While everything round there is charmingly neat.—
Yes, the children are home and as gay as a lark,
While the good mother greets us with pleasure;—but hark!
A baby-cry comes from the bedroom beyond,
And Jenny brings forth a sweet, sunny-haired blonde,

169

Saying: "This is the something we wanted to show you,
This two-years-old baby-girl—why, does she know you?
She holds out her hands to go to you so soon!"
"Ah! she feels we are friendly;—hear now her soft croon.
But how came she here, child?" "We found her just over
The lumber-yard fence, with a board for a cover,
Wrapped up in a blanket marked Bertha." "But why
Do you not to the charity mission apply?"
    "O, we want her ourselves! And the good Lord, through you,
{336} Has given us this home, so what else should we do,
Than to keep what He sends? And we're sure He sent Berty,
In place of our baby that died, little Myrtie!"

And here these poor people, so poor they were starving
When I found them a few months ago, were now halving
Their food and their home with this waif and with Benny—
For he was an orphan child left by his granny,
Who died in an attic just over their room,
In the tumble-down house they before-time called home;
Though they've four of their own, and the eldest is Jenny,
The little street-sweep who would not take the penny,
Yet they say, "Benny seems quite as much to belong here,
And be one of our children, as if he were born here."

O, how many rich homes where no child is given,
  Might be made, for poor orphans, an opening to Heaven!
{337} And how many, poorer, might seem to be rich,
  With a benny or Bertha to fill up the niche
That is left 'neath the hundreds of home-roofs all over.
Which the Lord has designed some poor orphan shall cover;
For He makes His home where His children are moored,—
And brings in His wealth where they live by His word;
And the meal and the oil there shall never be spent;—
What we give to the poor, to the Lord we have lent.
A baby to feed, is a baby to love,
A child in the house, "a well-spring" from above,—
And never forsaken, and ne'er begging bread,
Shall be those who take care that His lambs are well fed.

{338}

THE HERE, THERE AND EVERYWHERE FAMILY.

Z

I am always in a buzz,
  Though I'm never in a fret,
But I'm ever with a zealot in his zeal;
  I am in the zephyr-breath,
  Yet with zest have often met
The zero mark that brings the ice-man weal.

Y

I've to do with the yoke, but not with the ox;
  I help every priest in his prayer;
I am new every year, and in four months appear,
  While I yield to the yeoman a share.

X

I live in a Lexicon,
  I mark half a score;
I ride with a Mexican,
  In Texas, for lore,   {339}

W

I am in every wing, yet I'm not in a dove;
I wait in the swing to be tossed up above.

I live in the woods, and I perch on the wall;
I am in the wild waves, though I sail in a yawl.

V

I am mingled with your victuals, yet 'm never in your mouth;
I always lead the van and must forever stem the wave;
I grow in every gravel bed, East, West, or North, or South,
And although I'm with the living, you will find me in the
grave.

U

I live in the urn, but not in the vase,
I always can run, but I never can race.
I tumble and jump, but I can't hop nor skip;
I hide in your mouth, but I ne'er touch your lip.

T

I'm doubled up in a patty-pan,
   Yet I never saw a pie;
I hide in the boy's first pair of boots,
   Nor pass his mittens by.   {340}

S

I am always in sadness, yet never know grief;

Then, too, I'm in gladness, which gives me relief.
I know not the ocean, but swim in the sea,
And the stars and the sunshine were not, but for me.

R

I live at both ends of a river,
    My home is the center of art;
I am found in both arrows and quiver
    Yet I quietly rest in your heart.

Q

I lead the queen, yet never walk
    Without you (u) at my heels;
I laugh at every question queer,
    And joy in piggy's squeals.

P

I perch on every pepper-pod,
    I peer in every place;
I prance with every palfrey gay,
    Yet never run nor race.   {341}

O

Listen, children, and you'll hear me in the cooing of the dove;
    In the lowing of the kine and the crowing of the cocks;

I am in your joy and sorrow, and I come to you in love,
  And you will find me safely hidden in the middle of your box.

N

I live in the moon, yet I visit the sun,
I've twice blest the noon, and I've twice kissed the nun;
I was in the beginning, yes, double and treble,
And wherever's an end I am always in the middle.

M

I, too, live in the moon, yet I ne'er saw the sun;
I ne'er blessed the noon, and I ne'er kissed a nun.
I'm one of the many, and in at each mess,
Though I've never a penny, I'm not in distress.

L

I sing in every lullaby,
  I'm out in every squall;
I ring in every shilling piece,
  And roll in every ball.   {342}

K

I am baked in a cake, but I never see bread,
I can fork hay, and rake, but I can't lie in bed;
I can like, but not love; though no doe, I'm with the buck;

I'm in kite, but not in dove; and I'm always in luck.

J

I'm in a baby-jumper, and with joy I laugh and sing,
But I quickly find myself shut up in jail,
Where I pass my time in jokes, or perhaps in conjuring,
Till I lead the Judge, who says I'm "out on bail."

I

I live in an Inn, yet I never taste beer,
  I never smoke, chew, or use snuff;
I am seen in high life, yet I'm true to my wife,
  And now I have told you enough.

H

At the door of a hut I must stand, it is true,
  Yet of the king's household I'm one;
I revel in heather all wet with the dew,
  And yet I am never in fun.   {343}

G

I grow in grace, yet gayety
Would have no place except for me;
I greet the gardener with a grin,
E'en though I lie the grave within.

I'm with the King, yet shun the Queen;
I walk in grey, ah! yes in green;
I gleam in gold, yet live in gloom,
And at a wedding kiss the groom.

F

I am in the farmer's field,
    I am fresh in all his fruits;
I'm in all his forests wide,
    But I'm not in his pursuits.

E

Twice told, I'm in Eternity,
    And yet I live in time;
I eat and sleep in every place,
    Yet soar in the sublime.

D

I darken your doors and your windows,
    And if you are deaf, dumb, or blind,
You may know I am always quite ready,
    Your duds or your dainties to find.   {344}

C

176

Though I live in the ocean so blue,
  Yet I never am seen in the sea;
I can cast a sheet-anchor, 't is true,
  And captains depend upon me.

B

  I grow in the bean,
  And to beauty I lean,
And when buttercups bloom I am there;
  I bend the boy's bow,
  And the bugle I blow,
Till I wake the Kamtchatcadale bear.

A

I lead out the ape, and I'm seen in the glass;
I hide in the grape, and I'm found in the grass.
I was there in the garden when Adam was made,
Not to help them to sin, though I stood in their shade.
You can not have an apple, an orange, a pear,
But in each and in all, I must have my full share.
You can not eat nor speak, nay, nor hear, without me;
That I'm chief among my fellows, you all must agree.

{345}

QUIRKS.

A little word of letters five
  That means bound fast together;
Transpose but two, and you will find
  A scattering yon and hither.

    UNITE—UNTIE.

* * * * *

And now a word of letters four

Five perfect words will make,
If you transpose and rightly place
  'Tis true and no mistake.

    LEVI—LIVE—VILE—EVIL—VEIL.

* * * * *

    Now five are found,
    With spring and bound
A twist or turn to take,
    And ere we know,
    All in a row,
Five other words they make.
  The times are bad,
  The items sad,
The mites must meet their fate;
  To smite the rock
  Emits a shock
That hurls us from the gate.

    TIMES—ITEMS—MITES—SMITE—EMITS.

{346}

SOMEBODY'S BOY.

List to the ring of the midnight song!
    'Tis somebody's boy;
The winds give to every wild echo a tongue.
    Yes, somebody's boy;

The witch of the revel has waved her wand
    Over somebody's boy;
And the spirit of evil has clasped the hand
    Of somebody's boy.

Comes now a yell on the midnight air
    From somebody's boy;
Reckless, defiant, and devil-may-care,
    Is somebody's boy.

Foul is the bed, madly dark the dank cell,
    Where somebody's boy
Is writhing in torture, the veriest hell,
    Yet, somebody's boy.

Waiting and watching, a mother's eyes weep
    For somebody's boy;
The vigil, dear Father, O help her to keep!
    For somebody's boy.   {347}

178

Throw round him, and over, thy Spirit to save,—
   This somebody's boy,
Ere fiends for his lost soul shall hollow the grave
   Of somebody's boy.

Fill with thy Spirit, too, our hearts we pray,
   That somebody's boy
We may watch for, and snatch from the death-trodden way,
   Yes, somebody's boy.

{348}

THE LADDIE-AND-LASSIE BIRDS.

Come sit with me in the green-wood bower,
   While I sing you a song of love;—
      'Tis the song of the birds
      In the deep, wild woods,
   'Tis the song of the sweet ring-dove.

The laddie-bird says, "I have come to woo;"
And the lassie-bird, "Ah! coo, coo, coo, coo."   {349}

The laddie-bird says, "With a hope to win,"—
And the lassie-bird, "Coo, coo, that is no sin."

The laddie-bird says, "Together we'll dwell,"
And the lassie-bird says, "In the Linden dell."

The laddie-bird says, "And build our nest,"
And the lassie-bird says, "In the tree to the West."

The laddie-bird says, "And raise our brood,"
And the lassie-bird says, "In the sweet solitude."

The laddie-bird says, "Till they're fit to fly,"
And the lassie-bird, "Yes, to the blue, blue sky."

The laddie-bird says, "Let us hie away;"—
And the lassie-bird, "Yes, and begin to-day."

The laddie-bird says, "I will take this moss,"—
And the lassie-bird says, "And I, this floss."

{350}

The laddie-bird says, "And we'll love so true;"
And the lassie-bird, "Ah, yes, coo, coo, coo."

'Tis the old-new song that the birds have sung,
Aye, the birds of every race,
   Since the world was planned,
And came forth from the hand
   Of the Maker, aglow with grace.

'Tis the song they will sing till time is o'er,—

```
'Tis the stream that from Paradise gushed;
 And the music that flows
 When the love-light glows,
Will never, no, never be hushed.
```

{351}

{352}

[Footnote: "The great watchful I is over US through TIME and ETERNITY.]

CPSIA information can be obtained
at www.ICGtesting.com
Printed in the USA
LVHW041244280820
664156LV00005B/747